1 st ed.

The Dieting
Gourmet

Also by Eileen Reece

French Family Cooking
The Taste of Madeleines

The Dieting Gourmet

by Eileen Reece

London   George Allen & Unwin Ltd
Ruskin House   Museum Street

First published in 1976

ISBN 0 04 641028 7

Printed in Great Britain
in 11 point Times Roman
by Cox & Wyman Ltd
London, Fakenham and Reading

Contents

Acknowledgements.

My thanks to Mrs Audrey Eyton, Editor of Slimming Magazine Limited, for her helpful advice on personal calorie counting;

and also to

The Metropolitan Life Insurance Company for permission to use their Weight Calculation Tables.

Introduction

There is only one way to lose weight and that is Eat Less.
There is only one way to eat less and that is Eat Slowly.
There is only one way to eat slowly and that is Chew
Your Food until it dissolves in your mouth.

This is what racehorses do, and you never see a fat race-horse.

This is what peasants do to make a little go a long way.
Sit down on the roadside beside one eating his midday
meal in France, Italy, Greece or any country where
peasants are poor and work hard, and you will learn that it
is by eating slowly and chewing methodically that he makes
his hunk of bread with a piece of sausage, or head of garlic
cloves, satisfy his hunger and provide the energy to do a
day's work that would make any one else turn pale to
contemplate.

And this is the hardest part of slimming. The first two
days when your over-stretched stomach is shrieking for
food, you fall on your allotted portion like a wolf, gulp it
down and it does you no good at all. You immediately
start thinking about your next meal. But if instead you
chew your food thoroughly, it is amazing how satisfying a
little can be, and how much more you relish the flavour of it.

At the age of 8, stung by my sister's wounding remarks
concerning my enormous appetite, I became a Fletcheriser,
having read of a man who chewed each mouthful of food
40 times until it liquidised. I drove my sisters mad, and my
revenge was sweet. When my staunch friend and whist
partner Edna came to tea (she was $7\frac{1}{2}$) Fletcherising together
like two dwarf ruminants, we were invincible. We must
have been impressive too, because my mother, in self-
defence, took to Fletcherising secretly. It cured her life-long
indigestion and reduced her excess weight.

So take your time over your food, enjoy it, and stay slim. Food should still be one of the pleasures of life even when you are on a diet.

Don't make a penance of your diet. It can be a way of improving your culinary skill, as well as your appearance.

Don't forget that your hair, skin, teeth and looks in general can benefit from your diet as much as your figure.

Don't bolt your food. Chew every mouthful until it mixes thoroughly with the saliva in your mouth and practically disappears of its own accord. Saliva is the first of the digestive juices.

Don't sit down to a meal feeling exhausted, worried or over-excited. Take time to relax first.

Don't eat at all when you are angry.

Don't forget that consistencies are important. Crisp, crunchy foods are not only good for your teeth, they are more satisfying than soft over-refined foods which disappear too quickly.

Don't abuse salt, ever. When on a diet use lemon juice instead. As a condiment it replaces salt and contributes extra vitamins. Salt retains liquids in the body.

Don't cut out certain elements of food entirely, such as bread, potatoes, cereals, bacon, pork meat; these supply the vitamins necessary to produce energy and a healthy nervous system. Just control the quantities taken. Adopt the Balanced Diet as a regular way of eating. This enables you to satisfy your cravings before they take over.

Don't drink with your meals except a limited quantity at breakfast-time.

Don't overload your diet and your stomach with citrus fruits. While a certain amount is important to health, they do not suit everybody when taken in excessive quantities.

Don't neglect your liquid intake between meals. All good diets insist on a certain quantity of cold water being taken daily.

Don't try to stave off hunger pangs with innumerable cups of instant coffee instead of food. They will prove instant death to your diet programme.

Don't start a meal with soup. It stimulates the gastric juices and increases the appetite. Take it mid-morning instead as a meal in itself.

Don't cut out breakfast entirely. This is foolish. To do a morning's work on an empty stomach puts too much strain on your fund of energy.

Don't eat what my Lancashire charlady called a 'Lundun brepfuss . . . a cup a cold tea and a piece of burnt toass on the door-step'. Get up 15 minutes earlier, sit down to whatever you have for breakfast and eat it quietly.

Don't starve yourself all day and then eat an enormous dinner. It is wiser to eat like a racehorse – little and often.

Don't go on a diet that makes you miserable. Pick the one that suits your needs; there are enough to choose from.

Don't forget that exercise is the handmaiden of all diets. It stops the sag. So work out a routine of exercises and do them every morning. Better still, join a Yoga class; it is a great tonic both mental and physical.

Don't allow dieting to become an obsession. Once you have attained the desired weight and shape, maintain it with a good balanced diet, but don't continue losing weight out of sheer vanity. If you do your looks will suffer. Loss of weight shows first in your face and *then* on your hips.

Don't view the days on a diet with dismay. The purpose of this book is to give you interesting recipes for good food which will improve your looks and health in general.

Don't forget that the difficulties of dieting are mostly in the mind.

And don't start on any diet without your doctor's approval. Write out your intended programme and submit it to him, by post if necessary.

Chapter 1

Weight Calculation

Collecting diets is a pastime as popular as collecting antiques. But there the similarity ends, and the differences begin.

Triumphant friends can be just as reluctant to tell you where they bought their latest acquisition as they are forceful in their insistence that you try their own particular diet. They seem incapable of realising that the choice of a diet, which will govern an important aspect of your life for quite a time, is just as personal as the choice of a bookcase that is going to stand before you for a considerable number of years. Their enthusiasm throws objectivity to the winds.

There is only one person who can advise you objectively and wisely on the choice of a diet and that is your doctor, and while all the diets given in this book have been medically approved it is essential for each one to be approved *for the person who is to practise it*. One man's diet can be another man's dilemma.

We are all of us the victims of our habits and especially of our eating habits. Some of us cannot face life and the day's work without a substantial breakfast (and it is unwise to dismiss this silent demand), others need much less but have an alarm clock in their stomach which goes off at 11 a.m.; some need a full lunch and a light meal in the evening, others fall asleep in the afternoon if they eat more than a salad at midday. The natural demands alter with each person's physical character. So the first thing to determine is the type of eater you are, whether you need little and often and so go on a diet which gives you up to five meals a day, improving your health and figure at the same time, or whether you eat three meals a day and continue to do so on a diet which will enable you to lose weight just the same.

*Average weights for men and women
according to height and age*

Height (in Shoes)*	Weight in pounds (in indoor clothing)					
	Ages 20–24	Ages 25–29	Ages 30–39	Ages 40–49	Ages 50–59	Ages 60–69
WOMEN						
4 ft 10 in	102	107	115	122	125	127
4 ft 11 in	105	110	117	124	127	129
5 ft 0 in	108	113	120	127	130	131
5 ft 1 in	112	116	123	130	133	134
5 ft 2 in	115	119	126	133	136	137
5 ft 3 in	118	122	129	136	140	141
5 ft 4 in	121	125	132	140	144	145
5 ft 5 in	125	129	135	143	148	149
5 ft 6 in	129	133	139	147	152	153
5 ft 7 in	132	136	142	151	156	157
5 ft 8 in	136	140	146	155	160	161
5 ft 9 in	140	144	150	159	164	165
5 ft 10 in	144	148	154	164	169	†
5 ft 11 in	149	153	159	169	174	†
6 ft 0 in	154	158	164	174	180	†
MEN						
5 ft 2 in	128	134	137	140	142	139
5 ft 3 in	132	138	141	144	145	142
5 ft 4 in	136	141	145	148	149	146
5 ft 5 in	139	144	149	152	153	150
5 ft 6 in	142	148	153	156	157	154
5 ft 7 in	145	151	157	161	162	159
5 ft 8 in	149	155	161	165	166	163
5 ft 9 in	153	159	165	169	170	168
5 ft 10 in	157	163	170	174	175	173
5 ft 11 in	161	167	174	178	180	178
6 ft 0 in	166	172	179	183	185	183
6 ft 1 in	170	177	183	187	189	188
6 ft 2 in	174	182	188	192	194	193
6 ft 3 in	178	186	193	197	199	198
6 ft 4 in	181	190	199	203	205	204

* 1 inch heels for men and 2 inch heels for women.
† Average weights not determined because of insufficient data.

*Desirable weights for men and women
according to height and frame. Ages 25 and over*

Height (in Shoes)*	Weight in pounds (in indoor clothing) WOMEN		
	Small frame	Medium frame	Large frame
4 ft 10 in	92–98	96–107	104–119
4 ft 11 in	94–101	98–110	106–122
5 ft 0 in	96–104	101–113	109–125
5 ft 1 in	99–107	104–116	112–128
5 ft 2 in	102–110	107–119	115–131
5 ft 3 in	105–113	110–122	118–134
5 ft 4 in	108–116	113–126	121–138
5 ft 5 in	111–119	116–130	125–142
5 ft 6 in	114–123	120–135	130–146
5 ft 7 in	118–127	124–139	133–150
5 ft 8 in	122–131	128–143	137–154
5 ft 9 in	126–135	132–147	141–158
5 ft 10 in	130–140	136–151	145–163
5 ft 11 in	134–144	140–155	149–168
6 ft 0 in	138–148	144–159	153–174

*For girls between 18 and 25 subtract 1
pound for each year under 25*

	MEN		
	Small frame	Medium frame	Large frame
5 ft 2 in	112–120	118–129	126–141
5 ft 3 in	115–123	121–133	129–144
5 ft 4 in	118–126	124–136	132–148
5 ft 5 in	121–129	127–139	135–152
5 ft 6 in	124–133	130–143	138–156
5 ft 7 in	128–137	134–147	142–161
5 ft 8 in	132–141	138–152	147–166
5 ft 9 in	136–145	142–150	151–170
5 ft 10 in	140–150	146–160	155–174
5 ft 11 in	144–154	150–165	159–179
6 ft 0 in	148–158	154–170	164–184
6 ft 1 in	152–162	158–175	168–189
6 ft 2 in	156–167	162–180	173–194
6 ft 3 in	160–171	167–185	178–199
6 ft 4 in	164–175	172–190	182–204

* 1 inch heels for men and 2 inch heels for women.
Courtesy of the Metropolitan Life Insurance Company.

The next point to establish is what your normal weight should be. This can be calculated quite simply with the preceding charts.

A person's correct weight is worked out according to his sex, height and age, and is governed by his build, that is, whether he is of light, medium, or heavy bone structure.

The first set of tables give correct average weight, and the second set give the *ideal, desirable weight* that we should all strive to achieve and maintain, not only because it is medically desirable as being the one associated with the lowest mortality figures but also because it is when at this ideal weight that we all of us feel at our best and most energetic.

Being overweight brings with it a considerable slowing down of physical activity, and those who lead a sedentary life in any case must take a firm decision to be much more active, starting by walking more often than they take the car, and fetching things from upstairs rather than asking someone else to bring them. It is not the exercise itself that takes off the extra weight, but the energy expended during that exercise which burns up the body fat. When the intake of calories exceeds the expenditure of energy necessary to consume them, the excess which remains unconsumed builds up into fat which now has to be got rid of. *Repeat* Fat builds up when the intake of calories exceeds the expenditure of energy necessary to consume them.

At this point a strict reducing diet becomes urgently required to make the body burn up its excess fat, and so regain normal weight and re-establish the balance of intake of calories just sufficient to meet the expenditure of energy. This diet must be combined with exercise whose function is not only to expend energy but also to tone up the muscles which have become flabby from lack of use, to make them firm and so restore a trim outline to the figure, a state of being in which we all take justifiable pleasure and pride.

Normal children and adolescents do not get fat because their expenditure of energy is as unlimited as their voracious appetite. The balance is maintained because their constant expenditure of energy burns away their intake of calories as fast as it is supplied by the food consumed. There is no build-up, and the amount of exercise provided by their constant activity keeps their muscles firm and supple. The formation of puppy fat coincides with the period when puberty and its glandular changes make adolescents disinclined, for a time, to make any effort whatsoever that involves an expenditure of energy. This type of fat disappears of its own accord as soon as the glandular readjustment is completed and youth's natural inclination to activity returns. It is when the car mania hits them that the more pernicious form of fat establishes itself. Even the young should lead an active life if they eat heartily. Their present predilection for a diet of crisps and colas (fats and carbohydrates astronomic in calories), which does nothing to improve their complexions incidentally, is luckily balanced by a restlessness which keeps them constantly on the move. Otherwise their intake of calories not burned up by this activity would build up into fat.

For those of more advanced years excess weight must be dealt with in a radical fashion. There is only one way to take off fat and re-establish the *status quo*, and that is to consume this build-up of body fat by living off it, as the camel lives off the water in its hump. Go on a fast reducing, re-establishing diet and take *no more fats of any kind, in any disguise*, for a limited period. Your body's need for the necessary fat will then consume that which is available, those cosy little pads at the back of the hip-bones, that thick layer below the belly button (so easily rolled between the fingers and thumb and so difficult to massage away), the thickening jowls, the meaty upper arms and all the other disfigurements that the voracious stomach and consolatory cakes and coffees trail after them.

For this initial re-establishment of normal weight, a quick sure diet is needed, and there is no more effective one than the High Protein Diet supplemented by multiple vitamin pills which the doctor prescribes. This diet was originally created to deal with the difficulties businessmen find in dieting while eating in restaurants. It supplies all the energy needed by the high-powered executive (and just as much by the hard-slogging housewife). It can be practised at those insidious business lunches when the resulting state of euphoria, and decreased mental activity brought on by a digestive tract working double over-time, have caused many an error of judgement. If only for this reason diet should form part of the top executive's mode of living. 'Never,' said an eminent French banker to me at the start of my working life, 'make an important decision at a business luncheon. Make it the next morning on an empty stomach.'

A clear head comes from a clear digestive tract, and this is why the High Protein Diet insists (as ALL good diets do) on a considerable quantity of liquids being drunk daily. The right ones at the right time are essential.

In order to avoid confusion to American readers whose gallon, quart and pint measures are $\frac{4}{5}$ths of the Imperial gallon, quart and pint used in England, these quantities will be given also in fluid ounces which measure is common to both countries, thus: $\frac{1}{2}$ Imperial pint (28.30 cl) = 10 fluid ounces – half an American pint being 8 fluid ounces.

The quantity of cold water drunk daily in between meals should be $1\frac{3}{4}$ Imperial pints (1 litre), that is 35 fluid ounces, and in addition, four cups of unsweetened tea, coffee, herb teas, etc., all taken in between or after meals, excepting the cup of hot milk or tea at breakfast-time to waken up the digestion. The other exception is a glass of red wine which can be taken with dinner. It stimulates the gastric juices and so aids digestion. Dry red wine is much less costly in calories than sweet white wine, but counted it must be.

A large intake of liquids activates the liver and kidneys to deal efficiently with the waste matter of any diet, neutralising, for example, the acidity caused by a high protein diet and bringing as a result a feeling of well-being, increased energy and a clear skin.

On the usual long-term diet start by drinking three glasses of water between meals for the first three days and then build up to the given quantities. The H.P. or High Protein Diet insists that the dieter drinks a minimum of eight glasses of cold water each day in addition to as much tea and coffee (with a little skimmed milk, and no sugar) as possible. This quantity of water may seem enormous to those of us who have completely forgotten our childhood habits, but thinking of it as three water meals a day plus morning tea, after-lunch coffee and the usual office time-wasters, this is not as over-facing as it seems. In consolation this amount of liquid also cuts down the desire for food, and there are a number of other drinks to relieve the monotony, of which more later.

The High Protein Diet and the Astronaut's Diet (page 39) are the two most effective. The former can be practised for a limited period (say three weeks at a time) in the normal course of life until the dieter's correct weight is regained. The latter must in no circumstances be practised for more than three days at a time, and even then only when the dieter is in perfect health and able to take complete rest. Both of these diets are not only quick and effective, an assurance the dieter needs as a morale booster, but they are the easiest to practise. Having been calculated for you, no calorie counting is needed. Counting the calories comes later when normal weight has been established and the Balanced Diet is adopted. Then it becomes part of the game, not a penance, enabling dieters to eat whatever they wish, in limited quantities. A balanced diet is the sane, normal, healthy way of eating, which maintains the normal weight and keeps the dieter in perfect form. It provides all that the human body requires, the vitamins and minerals, the proteins, fats, alkaline foods and some carbohydrates, needed to maintain good health, and we do need them all in the right and proper quantities. While this, the Balanced Diet, will fulfil the needs of most people, alternative diets are given to suit more individual requirements and circumstances.

Shock or crash diets, such as no-restrictions-one-day-and-nothing-but-black-coffee-the-next, justify their name only too dangerously. To expect such a delicate and well-balanced mechanism as the human digestive tract to stand up to the shock of excess one day, sudden and complete deprivation the next, only to revert to excess on the third day, is to abuse good health and tempt providence. The strain inflicted on the digestion by crash diets is folly and against all the commonsense laws of both gastronomy and dieting.

A sane healthy diet depends for its success on good digestion, and good digestion depends for its success on free-flowing digestive juices, the most important of which is the first to come into action, saliva. When food is chewed saliva flows at the same time, mixing in with it, and when food is *well* chewed, the amount of saliva which mixes with it is sufficient to reduce this food to a state well on the way to being digested before it reaches the stomach, where the process is completed. Liquids, other than a small quantity of good wine, should not be drunk with meals because they dilute the digestive juices – wine stimulates them. Food bolted down, half-chewed and insufficiently mixed with saliva, is not only difficult to digest but much more of it is needed to satisfy the appetite. Pause for five minutes between courses and you will find that the inclination to continue eating decreases rapidly.

Next in importance to a good digestion is the importance of a balanced diet as a continued healthy way of eating which maintains the normal weight once it is regained. To continue reducing beyond this point through sheer vanity is futile and foolish. One look at the dried-up, middle-aged who live on a permanent diet of lamb cutlets and grapefruit is convincing. As age advances nature is merciful in insisting on a little more flesh under the skin to fill out the creases. What we have to watch out for is the excess which a natural slowing down of activities encourages. Only take off the surplus weight, that which laziness, psychological compensating, and plain greed have put on, then maintain the weight that is normal for your height and your age by consuming no more than the number of calories your expenditure of energy can burn up.

The return to a normal diet will of course bring with it an increased interest in food. Abstinence makes the stomach grow fonder some people find, while others lose their interest in food completely while on a diet. This is a pity, and makes imminent the danger of becoming a bore at dinner parties when, in these days of food consciousness, the matter is a subject of conversation.

Diet food and delicious food can be synonymous, especially in a controlled Balanced Diet. The small amounts of fats and carbohydrates allowed each day can be combined with the protein and alkaline foods to create many delicious and original dishes.

The recipes given in Chapters 5, 6 and 7 I evolved over years of catering to the demands of a husband whose gastronomic knowledge and appreciation of good food were a stimulus to my own. The fact that he was forced to live on a permanent diet for medical reasons in no way deprived us of delicious meals or lessened the success of our constant dinner parties. In fact, as a challenge to the imagination and creative ability of any woman interested in cooking I recommend cooking for a dieting gastronomist.

Good food should, of course, be accompanied by good wine. Providing that the amount taken is limited and included in the daily calorie count, wine can be enjoyed on the Balanced Diet. This limitation is a sound reason for savouring one glass of a good vintage wine instead of drinking several glasses of an inferior grade. A heightened appreciation of the advantages of quality over quantity is one of the bonuses of dieting. Limited quantities of good food and good wine taken slowly and thoroughly appreciated are infinitely more satisfying than large quantities of both in inferior quality. The fact that carefully chosen quality is at the same time beneficial to one's general health provides an added incentive to this way of eating.

With better health, increased energy and an improved figure, one begins to wonder *why* people continue to kill themselves slowly but surely by over-eating. Habit is largely responsible, aided by laziness. The more you eat the more you can eat, by the slow process of distending the stomach. In this state the inclination to move, much less take any exercise, disappears completely, and exercise is a necessary adjunct to dieting. Exercises carried out before an open window, just as much as walking, riding, swimming, golf, or tennis, expend the energy which burns up the calories, and at the same time keep muscles firm and the body contour trim and neat. The return of youthful suppleness and the feeling of well-being experienced with practise of the exercises given in Chapter 8 increases one's enthusiasm, and determination never 'to let oneself go' again. Burning up the calories has more advantages than one.

Chapter 2

Calorie Counting and Calorie Chart

Calorie consumption is calculated simply. One pound of fatty tissue is the equivalent in energy of approximately 3,500 calories, so every time you eat 3,500 calories less than you expend, over a period of days, you should use up a pound of fatty tissue. Thus cutting out 500c a day would lead to a weight loss of one pound each week, and that is 52 pounds easily lost in a year. This gives a general idea of how simple it can be.

But much unconscious cheating goes on, mostly by people who imagine that they are following the rules very strictly, and this is what causes the complications. The most popular misconception is that all protein foods are non-fattening, and people eat huge steaks and quantities of fish and cheese to fill up, virtuously cutting out bread, cakes and all starches which they *know* are fattening. But all food has a calorie count and meat, however lean, contains a certain amount of fat and so does fish, hence the reason for cooking them both as explained in Chapter 7.

Beware of the diet which says, 'You may eat freely of meat, fish and cheese of any kind.' It will leave you satisfied in both stomach and conscience but it will also leave you wondering why you are losing so little weight. Cheeses can vary in calorie count from 30c to 232c per ounce, so study the calorie counting chart for all foods and beverages given at the end of this chapter. You will very soon become conversant with it.

The object of a diet is not only to lessen the consumption of high calorie foods choosing low calorie foods instead, but also to control the intake of calories generally either by weight or by the size of the portion, choosing a steak roughly the size and thickness of a woman's palm and not an entire slice of sirloin in the self-delusion that 'lean meat doesn't count'. It all counts.

Considering the fact that the majority of people regularly make off with well over 3,500 calories a day, which is 1,000 in excess of what they need, it is no wonder that they look and feel heavy, and blench at the suggestion of a walk.

This habit of over-eating makes sense of the general rule that by cutting your usual daily calorie intake by one-third you are bound to lose weight. And it is as much the way you feel as the way you look that is the most valid reason for dieting. A period of sensible dieting can always be recommended as a general pick-me-up, even for the healthiest person. Calorie-counting is not the food crank's pastime that many people think it is. A calculated calorie intake is the means of making certain that excess weight, once taken off by a fast-reducing diet, never returns, and yet this method enables you to eat anything your fancy dictates.

Fifteen hundred calories a day is generally recognised as the number on which the average woman should start dieting, decreasing to 1,200 if necessary after eight or ten days' trial, until the desired weight is achieved. A very active person would not need to decrease, while a sedentary person might . . . this need must be judged by each individual and controlled by regular weight recording.

The equivalent figure for men would be 1,700 to 1,800 calories a day, increasing or decreasing slightly according to how active a person he is . . . again the necessity is judged by weight control, and how the individual, man or woman, reacts to dieting. There is no doubt that once we become used to eating less, and eating the right food, we all of us have much more energy and enjoy life infinitely more than when eating more than we require.

Once the desirable weight is achieved the Balanced Diet should be adopted as a regular healthy way of eating. This for the average woman should comprise between 1,800 to 2,200 calories a day according to her mode of life, sedentary or active, and for a man approximately 2,700 calories, also according to his daily activities. This number of calories does not, of course, constitute a rigid law. When the diet is varied to include all health-giving food, the calorie intake will fluctuate slightly, but it will be well guided by the new outlook we acquire when dieting and the fact, beyond doubt, that we are satisfied with much less when eating the right and proper food in the right way. With regular exercise the Balanced Diet will maintain the desirable weight permanently.

The increased number of calories this regular diet allows should be spent wisely for nutritional benefit, on such meats as liver, kidneys, brains and sweetbreads, on eggs, milk, cheese, fresh citrus fruit juices, raw vegetables and fruit and extra wheatgerm, and not on carbohydrates such as cakes, biscuits and buns.

In dieting you must watch the portions as carefully as you count the calories – the thicker the slice the smaller it should be. Acquire a good diet scale which gives the weights in ounces and their equivalent in grammes, and when you have weighed a diet portion of meat, fish and cooked vegetables a few times, you will soon learn to judge them at a glance.

A diet portion of meat weighs a minimum of $3\frac{1}{2}$ ounces, that is 100 grammes.

A diet portion of fish weighs between 5 and 6 ounces, say 160 grammes. This is for white or lean fish.

'Fat' fish such as salmon, mackerel and herrings, should be cut to much smaller quantities, that is approximately $3\frac{1}{2}$ ounces or 100 grammes. Dieters should eat no fried fish whatsoever, only that which is steamed, grilled or baked.

A diet portion of cheese eaten as a main course should not exceed 2 ounces, say 56 grammes, that is, a piece $\frac{1}{2}$ inch thick and 2 inches by 3 inches; this is for cheese in the average calorie count such as Dutch Edam (a good dieter's cheese). If cheese of high fat content is chosen, like cream cheese or Camembert, then the quantity should be halved.

A diet portion of each vegetable is $3\frac{1}{2}$ ounces (100 g), represented by 2 heaped tablespoons. Two different varieties are allowed at each of the two main meals. They can be replaced by a very generous serving of green salad of mixed kinds, equal to a firm heart of lettuce, the size of a large orange.

A diet portion of fruit is 5 ounces (141.74 g), that is, 3 heaped tablespoons.

A diet portion of skimmed milk is $\frac{1}{2}$ Imperial pint per day for all uses (10 fluid ounces = 28.3 centilitres).

A portion of fats taken as a daily minimum on the Balanced Diet is 1 teaspoonful of butter and 1 dessert-spoonful of oil, either olive oil or non-saturated oils such as corn, sunflower seed or safflower seed oil, if the latter are recommended in preference by the doctor.

A diet portion of wholewheat bread should not exceed 4 thin slices a day.

Sugar should be kept to a minimum (that is when it is allowed by the diet) using brown sugar in preference to white, and honey instead, whenever possible. Sugar, while counting high in calories, has very little nutritional value and should be regarded solely as a flavouring.

In order to simplify the conversion of ounces into grammes as far as diet portions are concerned, most of the following weights given can be approximated to the rounded number of grammes. Thus the average diet portion of meat, poultry or game which is between 3 and 4 ounces ($3\frac{1}{2}$ oz equals 99.22 g) can be rounded to 100 grammes.

Conversion Table for Ounces to Grammes

1 ounce =	28.35 grammes	
$1\frac{1}{2}$ ounces =	42.52 grammes	
2 ounces =	56.70 grammes	
$2\frac{1}{2}$ ounces =	70.87 grammes	
3 ounces =	85.05 grammes	
$3\frac{1}{2}$ ounces =	99.22 grammes (can be rounded to 100 g)	
4 ounces =	113.40 grammes	
$4\frac{1}{2}$ ounces =	127.57 grammes	
5 ounces =	141.74 grammes	
$5\frac{1}{2}$ ounces =	155.92 grammes (can be rounded to 156 g)	
6 ounces =	170.09 grammes	

1 fluid ounce = 2.83 centilitres (can be rounded to 3 cl)
(1 fluid ounce is the equivalent of 2 tablespoons)
8 fluid ounces = 22.68 centilitres = $\frac{1}{2}$ pint American measure

The following indications for judging diet portions will be useful when you are not eating in your own home:

Fish

Sole or plaice, grilled	2 large fillets
Turbot or halibut, grilled	1 slice 4 inches by $2\frac{1}{2}$ inches, $\frac{1}{2}$ inch thick
Cod, grilled	1 medium steak 3 inches in diameter, $\frac{1}{2}$ inch thick

Beef

Steak, grilled	3 inches square, $\frac{3}{4}$ inch thick
Liver	1 medium slice 4 inches square, $\frac{1}{4}$ inch thick
Roast	1 large thin slice 6 inches by 4 inches
Tongue	2 medium slices, cut thin
Calf's liver	1 medium slice 4 inches square, $\frac{1}{4}$ inch thick
Veal, roast	1 medium slice 4 inches by 3 inches, $\frac{1}{4}$ inch thick
Veal cutlet	as for steak
Veal kidney	half of a large one

Lamb

Chop, grilled	1 small 2 inches square, $\frac{1}{2}$ inch thick
Roast	2 small slices $2\frac{1}{2}$ inches by 2 inches, $\frac{1}{4}$ inch thick
Kidneys	2 average size
Mutton chop, grilled	1 small 3 inches by 2 inches, less thick than lamb
Mutton, boiled	half the quantity of roast lamb

Chicken

Roast	2 slices breast 4 inches by 3 inches, medium thin or 1 medium thigh or 1 large drumstick
Boiled	half the quantity of roast
Poussin, grilled	half a small bird
Livers	2 whole, large size

Turkey

Roast	1 large slice breast

Game

As for roast chicken breast
In the case of small game, grouse, etc., as for poussin

In all cases no fat, skin, gravy or stuffing should be served with diet portions of meat.

Two eggs will replace any of the above portions of meat.

While all cereals and starches should be kept to a minimum, rice in small quantities is not only satisfying to a hungry stomach but it also looks a lot. A serving of 2 tablespoonsful only costs 70c.

The same applies to a potato baked in its jacket. One medium size potato is valued at 90c.

Wheatgerm, while classed as carbohydrate, is a food rich in protein and vitamin B. One heaped tablespoon each day sprinkled over yoghurt, salads and fruit should be part of everybody's diet, especially when they have turned forty years of age.

Though citrus fruit juices such as orange, grapefruit and lemon in their natural unsweetened state perform the function of helping the breakdown of fats into digestible elements, and are therefore useful diet allies, all juices both fresh and tinned varieties carry a certain calorie count, so watch the quantities. Lemon, however, has a minimal calorie count. All juices when squeezed should be served with just the pips removed, and not strained. The small flecks of pulp left in augment their already high vitamin content.

Water has no calorie count at all and the only other items of food which carry none, or so minute a calorie count that they may be termed nil, are coffee, tea and tisanes or herb teas, lemon juice, vinegar, salt, culinary herbs and mineral oil which is commonly called liquid paraffin in England. The use of this oil has the disadvantage, however, of robbing the consumer of the fat soluble vitamins A, D and E, and is therefore not advisable as a continued practice. Mustard and pepper have the highest calorie count of all condiments (132 and 88 to the ounce respectively) but the amount taken is so small as to be negligible.

In the following charts the number of calories given corresponds to the average diet portion of food ... meat $3\frac{1}{2}$ oz (100 g), fish $5\frac{1}{2}$ oz (156 g), etc., and in the case of high calorie foods which must be taken sparingly when on a diet (nuts, fats, etc.) the quantities are given in single ounces (28.35 g).

Other quantities given are:

1 bc: large breakfastcup = $\frac{1}{2}$ Imp. pint (28.3 cl) = 10 fl. oz
1 cup: teacup = $\frac{1}{3}$ Imp. pint (18.86 cl) = $6\frac{1}{3}$ (spare) fl. oz
1 glass: $\frac{1}{2}$ Imp. pint — (28.3 cl) = 10 fl. oz
1 small glass: gill = $\frac{1}{4}$ Imp. pint (14.15 cl) = 5 fl. oz
1 wineglass: approx. $3\frac{1}{2}$ fl. oz (10.5 cl)
1 tbs: tablespoon (28.35 g) = 1 oz solids (5 tbs liquid = $\frac{1}{2}$ fl. oz)
1 dsp: dessertspoon (14.15 g) = $\frac{1}{2}$ oz solids
1 tsp: teaspoon (7.08 g) = $\frac{1}{4}$ oz solids

Calorie Chart

MEAT, POULTRY, GAME, FISH AND EGGS
Beef

	Calories per diet portion $3\frac{1}{2}$ oz = 100 g
Steak, grilled	301
raw	177
Roast (no fat, skin or gravy)	248
Boiled Silverside	301
Topside	213

Lamb	*Calories per diet portion* $3\frac{1}{2}$ *oz* = *100 g*
Chop, grilled, lean only	271
Roast (no fat, skin or gravy)	292
Boiled (mutton)	260
Liver, grilled 2 minutes	143
Kidneys	124

Veal

Roast (no skin or gravy)	232
Escaloppe	216
Liver grilled 2 minutes	143
fried	262
Kidney, grilled	124

Pork

Roast leg (no crackling, skin or gravy)	317
loin (no crackling, skin or gravy)	284
Chop, grilled, lean only	325
Ham, boiled, lean only	219
lean and fat	435
1 large slice lean, cut thin	137
Bacon, grilled, 2 thin slices	95
1 Pork sausage, grilled, 2 oz (56.7 g)	188
Black pudding, grilled, 2 oz (56.7 g)	164

Poultry and Game

Duck, breast meat only	313
Turkey	196
Rabbit, casseroled	180
Chicken, roast (no skin, fat or gravy)	189
Boiling fowl	203
Game	213 to 233
Hare, roast	193

2 eggs replace any diet portion of meat. Other substitutes of equivalent nutritional value are: 1 bc whole milk

2 bc skimmed milk

2 bc buttermilk

$\frac{2}{3}$ bc cottage cheese

Fish
Calories per diet portion
$5\frac{1}{2}$ *oz* $= 156$ *g*

Non-fat fish, such as bass, trout, cod, turbot, red and grey mullet, grayling, etc.	165
Other fat fish, such as mackerel, fresh sardines	275
Salmon	330
Herring	368
Haddock, smoked	154
Tunnyfish in oil	412
Sardines in oil	440

Shellfish

Shrimps	176
Mussels	137
Crab meat	198
Lobster	187

Eggs
Calories

1 Raw egg	76 to 80
1 Yolk, raw	61
1 White cooked	16
1 Soft-boiled	77 to 80
1 Fried	110

2 portions of the above foods are allowed daily according to choice

VEGETABLES
Calories per $3\frac{1}{2}$ oz (100 g)

Artichokes, fresh leaf variety, cooked	15
Jerusalem variety, cooked	19
Asparagus, fresh, 6 medium	20
tinned	20
frozen	40
Aubergines (eggplant), baked in skin	15
Beans, broad, cooked	43
raw	266

Calories per 3½ oz (100 g)

French, cooked	7
haricot	89
runner, cooked	7
Beetroot, raw	28
cooked	44
Broccoli, cooked	14
Brussels sprouts, raw	32
cooked	16
Cabbage, red, raw	20
Spring, cooked	8
Winter, raw	25
cooked	8
Carrots, raw	23
cooked	21
Cauliflower, raw	25
cooked	11
Celery, raw	9
cooked	11
Celeriac, raw	18
cooked	14
Chicory, raw	9
Cucumber, raw	9
Endive, raw	11
Leeks, raw, 3 small	30
cooked	25
Lentils, cooked	96
Marrow	7
Mushrooms, raw	7
cooked in butter	217
Onions, raw	23
boiled	13
Spring, raw	36
Olives in brine	106
Parsley	21
Parsnips, raw	49
cooked	64
Peas, fresh cooked	49
frozen cooked	70
dried cooked	100
tinned	86
Potatoes, boiled	80
mashed	120

Calories per 3½ oz (100 g)

baked in jacket	90
roast	123
new boiled	75
Radishes	15
Salads: Lettuce	12
Mustard & Cress	10
Watercress	15
Spinach, fresh, frozen or tinned	26
Swedes, raw	21
cooked	18
Sweetcorn	85
Tomatoes, raw	14
Turnips, cooked	15
Turnip tops, cooked	11

4 portions of the above food can be eaten daily

FRUIT

Calories per portion
5 oz (141.74 g)

Apples, eating, raw	65
cooking, baked without sugar	45
Apricots, fresh	40
cooked	30
Avocado pear, half large	125
Banana, large	110
Blackberries, raw	40
cooked without sugar	30
Blackcurrants, raw	40
cooked without sugar	30
Cherries, raw	65
cooked without sugar	50
Figs, fresh	60
dried, cooked without sugar	150
Gooseberries, raw	25
cooked without sugar	20
Grapes, black	70
white	90
Grapefruit	15
Lemons	10
Mandarines and tangerines, fresh	35
tinned	90

	Calories per portion *5 oz (141.74 g)*
Melon, cantaloupe	35
honeydew	30
Nectarines	65
Oranges	50
Peaches, fresh	54
tinned	95
Pears, eating, raw	55
cooking, without sugar	40
tinned	90
Pineapple, fresh	65
tinned	90
Plums, raw	35
cooked without sugar	30
Raspberries, raw	35
cooked without sugar	35
Rhubarb, cooked without sugar	5
Strawberries	35

2 portions of the above fruits are allowed daily according to choice

The following high calorie foods are listed in calories to the single ounce

Dried Fruits and Nuts (shelled)

	Calories per 1 oz (28.35 g)
Almonds	170
Brazil nuts	183
Chestnuts	49
Cobnuts	113
Coconut (fresh)	104
(desiccated)	178
Peanuts	171
Walnuts	156
Apricots, dried, raw	52
cooked without sugar	17
Currants	69
Raisins	70
Sultanas	71
Dates	70

Calories per 1 oz (28.35 g)

Figs, dried, raw	61
cooked without sugar	30
Peaches, dried, raw	61
cooked without sugar	20
Prunes, dried, raw	46
cooked without sugar	19

Dried fruits and nuts are of such high calorie count they should be eaten in very small quantities, but also being of high vitamin and mineral content, they may be eaten as a meal in themselves, occasionally.

CEREALS AND CEREAL FOODS

Calories per portion
1 oz (28.35 g)

All Bran	88
Barley, cooked	34
Biscuits, sweet	158
plain	123
rusks	116
cream crackers	158
Bread, white	69
wholemeal	68
1 average size white roll	130
1 ryecrisp diet biscuit	
$2 \times 3\frac{1}{2}$ inches	25
Cornflakes and Shredded Wheat	104
Grapenuts	102
Oatmeal, raw	115
cooked as porridge	13
Pastas, macaroni, spaghetti, etc., boiled	32
Rice, boiled	35
Wheatgerm	101

The above foods should be eaten as little as possible, except when on the Balanced Diet, when wholemeal bread, oatmeal porridge either raw or cooked, and an occasional serving of rice can be included. Wheatgerm should be taken daily in a minimum quantity of $1\frac{1}{2}$ heaped table-spoonsful.

FATS

	Calories per 1 oz (28.35 g)
Bacon, grilled	169
Butter	226
1 tps =	56
Cream, double	131
single	62
1 tbs double =	50
1 tbs single =	35
Dripping	262
Lard	262
Mayonnaise (made with olive oil and egg yolk)	324
1 dsp =	108
Oil, olive or nut	264
1 dsp =	88

On a good balanced diet a minimum of 1 teaspoonful of butter and 1 dessertspoonful of oil daily are essential, and can both be used either in the raw state or for cooking.

SUGARS

	Calories per 1 oz (28.35 g)
Sugar, white and brown	112
1 tsp =	28
1 dsp =	80
Honey	82
1 dsp =	27
Jam	74
1 dsp =	24
Jelly (preserve)	74
1 dsp =	24
Chocolate, milk	167
plain	155

The above should only be taken very sparingly

MILK AND DAIRY PRODUCTS

Calories

Milk, fresh, whole 10 oz glass (24 cl)	190
skimmed, liquid 10 oz glass (24 cl)	100
powdered, whole, 1 oz (8 g)	150
skimmed, 1 oz (8 g)	93
condensed, whole, tinned unsweetened, 1 oz (28 g)	45
condensed, whole, tinned sweetened, 1 oz (28 g)	100
condensed, skimmed, sweetened, 1 oz (28 g)	76
Buttermilk, 1 large breakfastcup	90
Ice cream, 3½ oz (100 g)	196
Yoghurt, plain, whole milk, individual carton (5 fl. oz or 15 cl approx.)	100
plain, low fat milk	60
plain, fat free, goat's milk	20

Cheese

Cottage (curd)	30
Cream	232
Camembert	175 to 230
	(according to fat content)
Cheshire	110
Cheddar	120
Dutch Edam	88
Roquefort	90
Gorgonzola	112
Stilton	135
Gruyère	132

2 portions of milk, cheese or yoghurt are allowed daily according to the diet

These calorie counts are also given in 1 oz units (28.35 g), one ounce constituting a serving, or two ounces if taken as a main course. This of course excludes curd cheese, which is of very low calorie count.

BEVERAGES	*Calories*
Beer, bottled or draught, 8 fluid ounces (22.68 cl)	80 to 110
Brandy, 1 fluid ounce (approx. 3 cl)	63
Broth, vegetable, 1 bc	30
beef (well skimmed)	36
chicken (well skimmed)	56
Chocolate, 1 bc (or cocoa with milk)	255
Coffee, black, 1 bc	nil
with milk, 1 bc	87
Cider, dry, 1¾ pints (1 litre or 35 fl. oz)	418
sweet	480
Coca Cola, 1 glass (6½ fluid ounces)	80
Champagne, 1 champagne glassful	91
Ginger ale, soda water, tonic (individual bottles)	45 to 60

Juices

Apricot, 1 small glass, ¼ Imp. pint (15 cl or 5 fl. oz.)	80
Apple, 1 small glass	62
Grape, 1 small glass	82
Grapefruit, fresh unsweetened	42
tinned	60
Orange, fresh or tinned	60
Lemon	30
Pineapple, unsweetened	60
Vegetable, mixed	49
Liqueurs, all kinds, small liqueur glass	100 to 115
Dry Martini (gin and French vermouth)	135
Sherry, dry, 3½ fluid ounces (10.5 cl)	116
sweet	133
Tea	nil
Tisanes (herb teas)	nil
Vermouth, all kinds, 3½ fluid ounces (10.5 cl)	110
Vodka, 1 fluid ounce (3 cl)	63
Gin, 1 fluid ounce (3 cl)	55
Whisky, 1 fluid ounce (3 cl)	58
(1 fluid ounce = 2 tablespoons)	

Wines

Red or white, dry: *Calories*

    1 litre bottle ($1\frac{3}{4}$ Imp. pint or 35 fl. oz)   700

    1 wineglassful, dry (approx. $3\frac{1}{2}$ fl. oz

    or 10.5 cl)   70

    1 wineglassful, sweet   105

To lose weight it is necessary to drink a daily minimum of $1\frac{3}{4}$ Imperial pints (1 litre or 35 fluid ounces) of water in between meals plus tea, coffee and tisanes after meals, but never with them.

The calorie, or more correctly, the kilocalorie kCal (often written as Calorie with a cap 'C') was formerly used as the nutritional energy unit. It will take some time for everyone to be familiar with the internationally adopted new system for nutritional energy units – namely the kilojoule (kj). Both units (kCal and kj) will be used for a while until kj become generally known. Already nutritionists are working in the new system. Conversion from calories to joules is done by multiplying by the factor 4.186 (usually rounded up to 4.2).

Chapter 3

Ten Different Diets

If you are very much overweight or if you need to take off in a hurry the few extra pounds that we all seem to accumulate during the winter, the first three diets given will suit the requirements perfectly. They give the quickest results.

Less stringent alternatives follow for those whose problem is less urgent, and the last diet given, the Balanced Diet, is recommended as a healthy way of eating once the desired weight is achieved in order to maintain it permanently.

Whatever the diet weigh yourself regularly twice a week. Too frequent visits to the scales take the edge off the surprise.

In all the diets given, 1 glass indicates $\frac{1}{2}$ Imperial pint (28.35 cl) which is 10 fluid ounces. One large cup is the same quantity as 1 glass. The coffee, tea, mint tea, etc., to be taken after meals, refers to a teacup (unless otherwise indicated), that is, $\frac{1}{3}$ Imperial pint (18.86 cl) or $6\frac{1}{3}$ fluid ounces.

The H.P. Diet (High Protein)

No fats whatsoever, no alcohol, no sugar, no starches, no vegetables, no salads, no fruit, 1 glass skimmed milk daily, a little cottage cheese.

Grilling is the method of cooking recommended and not frying (see page 102).

Lean red meats (beef, liver, veal and lamb), chicken, turkey, game (no duck or goose), fish of the non-fat varieties (sole, plaice, turbot, cod, hake, halibut; no salmon, mackerel or sardines).

Eggs, hard or soft-boiled or poached (*never* fried or cooked in any fat). Eight glasses of cold water daily in between meals and as much weak tea or coffee as desired after meals, taken with a little skimmed milk. Mint tea is suggested as an alternative (page 58).

SAMPLE MENUS

On waking up   1 glass of hot water sipped as hot as possible, while still in bed

Breakfast   2 soft-boiled or hard-boiled eggs (the latter are the more sustaining, taking longer to digest)
One or two large cups of tea or coffee with a little skimmed milk

Mid-morning   2 glasses of cold water, at intervals

Lunch   Portion of non-fat fish grilled, and seasoned with soy sauce and black pepper
Small helping of cottage (curd) cheese
Two cups of Mint Tea

Mid-afternoon   2 glasses of cold water

Dinner   Half an hour before dinner drink another glass of cold water
1 sliced hard-boiled egg
1 portion of grilled steak, or liver cooked in a non-stick surfaced pan without fat, or baked chicken or game served without skin or gravy
Small portion of Coffee Curd (page 93)
Large cup of tea or coffee with a little skimmed milk

Before retiring   2 glasses of cold water

This diet should be supplemented by vitamin pills according to doctor's prescription.

The Astronaut's Diet

The Astronaut's Diet is most rewarding, but it must *on no account* be practised for more than 3 days at a time, and then only when in perfect health and when it is possible to rest a great deal, i.e. late mornings in bed, no strenuous work, cat-naps in the afternoon and early nights.

On waking up	1 glass of hot water with a squeeze of lemon juice, sipped as hot as possible while still in bed
Breakfast	1 hard-boiled egg Tea or coffee with $1\frac{1}{2}$ tablespoons of powered skimmed milk
Mid-morning	2 glasses of cold water
Lunch	1 large heart of lettuce with L.P. Diet Dressing made without herbs (page 65) Weak tea with lemon juice, or coffee without milk or sugar
Mid-afternoon	2 glasses of cold water
Dinner	Half an hour before dinner drink another glass of cold water 1 slice of lean roast beef or grilled steak weighing not more than $3\frac{1}{2}$ oz (100 g) Salad as at lunch-time Tea or coffee without milk or sugar, or Mint Tea
Before retiring	2 glasses of cold water

As much tea, coffee or mint tea as desired may be taken during the day provided it is taken as indicated after meals.

The 900 Calorie Diet

The third rapid-results diet is less severe than the Astronaut's, but it must be practised in the same conditions of rest and for no more than 7 days running.

900 calories of fat-free food and 1 litre ($1\frac{3}{4}$ Imperial pints or 35 fluid ounces) of bottled mineral water such as Evian, Vichy, San Pellegrino or Source Badoit are parcelled out daily in the following way.

On waking up	1 glass of mineral water
Breakfast	1 carton goat's milk yoghurt (obtainable at health food shops)
Mid-morning	1 glass mineral water
Lunch	1 heart of raw celery and 8 radishes $5\frac{1}{2}$ oz (156 g) crab or lobster meat sprinkled with paprika and lemon juice 1 5 oz portion (141 g) green beans (page 83) 1 large apple 1 glass mineral water
Mid-afternoon	1 glass mineral water
Dinner	2 tbs cottage (curd) cheese flavoured with chopped mint, chives and black pepper 4 oz (113.4 g) lean grilled steak 2 large halves grilled tomato sprinkled with lemon juice 1 portion summer vegetables (page 83) sprinkled with $1\frac{1}{2}$ tbs wheatgerm A portion of black grapes (eat skins and pips) 1 glass mineral water
Before retiring	The rest of the mineral water

The No Starch Diet

This next diet, based on the elimination of all carbohydrates, does however, give a greater variety in the choice of foods than the previous ones.

No bread, no potatoes, no pastries, no biscuits, no sugar, no spaghetti, rice, macaroni or other pasta.

Some dairy produce, butter (very little), skimmed milk, and yoghurt.

Lean meats and fish, chicken and turkey without skin or gravy.

Salads, fruit and vegetables (excepting avocado pear and bananas).

SAMPLE MENUS

On waking up   1 glass of hot water with the juice of half a lemon, sipped as hot as possible while in bed

Breakfast   1 glass of hot skimmed milk flavoured with coffee or tea,

or

2 small cartons plain yoghurt

Mid-morning   2 glasses of cold water at intervals

Lunch   1 large slice breast of roast chicken, no skin or gravy
1 firm heart of lettuce with L.P. Dressing (page 65)
1 orange or half a grapefruit
Tea with lemon, or coffee with a little skimmed milk

Mid-afternoon   1 large cup of tea with lemon, and later
1 glass of cold water

Dinner   Half an hour before dinner 1 glass of cold water
1 medium slice of calf's or lamb's liver grilled with $\frac{1}{2}$ teaspoon butter and lemon juice

or

a medium serving of steak or fish grilled in the same way
1 large grilled Devilled Tomato (page 86)

and

2 heaped tablespoons Brussels Sprouts (page 84)
2 cups of Mint Tea (page 58)

Before retiring   1 glass of cold water

The Rabbit's Diet

For those people whose disposition makes them want to nibble continually, this next diet is ideal. It provides five meals a day.

No butter, margarine or sugar, a little olive oil, a little bread.

Skimmed milk, eggs, unfermented cheeses (Edam, Cheddar, Cheshire – no Camembert or Brie).

Lean meats and fish, poultry, game.

Salads, fruit and vegetables.

1 litre bottle Vichy water per day.

SAMPLE MENUS

On waking up 1 large cup of china tea with lemon sipped as hot as possible while still in bed

Breakfast 1 poached, scrambled or soft-boiled egg
1 thin slice of toast
Tea or coffee with a little skimmed milk

Mid-morning 1 large glass of Vichy water
1 orange or half a grapefruit, or the fresh juice of either

Lunch 1 slice lamb's liver or slice of lean boiled ham
Tomato and Cucumber Salad with French Dressing (pages 69–70) and 2 heaped tbs green vegetables
2 ryecrisp biscuits
Small glass of skimmed milk, or coffee with skimmed milk

Mid-afternoon 1 apple, or orange or half grapefruit
Later, 2 glasses of Vichy water

Dinner A portion of grilled steak or small lamb chop
or
A portion of Fish Pie (page 99)
Mixed green salad (watercress, lettuce,

endive) with Diet Dressing Nos 1 or 2
(page 67)
1 slice of bread or 2 ryecrisp biscuits
1 tangerine or pear
Lemon Tisane (page 58)

Before retiring   The rest of the Vichy water

The Young Mother's Diet

To rid young mothers of that excess weight which has
accumulated during pregnancy, French doctors prescribe
the following slimming diet which pays particular attention
to the calcium intake. As well as the foods indicated, pills
are prescribed to compensate for the lack of salt. Its use is
not missed in the seasonings when plenty of lemon juice
and fresh herbs are used instead, which also build up the
intake of vitamins.

No bread, no starches, no alcohol and no salt.

To compensate, plenty of dairy produce, especially milk
and unfermented cheeses (for the calcium), sweetbreads
and all kinds of liver, eggs, lentils, oysters, apricots (for the
iron) and all green leaf vegetables which are an additional
source of this mineral, plenty of all vegetables and fruit.

Lean red meats, lean pork, poultry.

2 teaspoons of honey per day.

The butter should be *unsalted*.

SAMPLE MENUS

On waking up   A large cup of weak china tea with lemon,
sipped as hot as possible while in bed

Breakfast   A large cup of hot or cold milk flavoured
with tea or coffee
A slice of Gruyère cheese and a hard-
boiled egg

Mid-morning   A large cup of Chicken Consommé (page
106) and later 1 glass of cold water

Lunch   Sweetbreads or chicken livers, cooked with
$\frac{1}{2}$ tsp of butter

or
Portion of steak grilled rare with lemon juice
6–8 fresh asparagus spears with Lemon Sauce (page 85)
2 tbs spinach or Beer and Cabbage Salad (page 74)
1 small slice Cheddar, Cheshire or Dutch cheese
Fresh strawberries, cherries or apricots (in winter 1 orange or 2 tangerines)
Mint Tea

Mid-afternoon   Several cups of weak china tea with lemon, later 1 glass of cold water

Dinner   Half an hour before dinner, 1 glass of cold water
6 green olives
Mixed green salad (lettuce, batavia, escarole and green pepper with French Dressing) (page 69)
Slice of grilled calf's liver (brushed with melted butter)
2 tablespoons french beans liberally sprinkled with parsley
Half a large grapefruit, or a Compôte of Apricots (page 93)
Camomile Tisane (page 58)

Before retiring   1 glass of cold water, or hot and flavoured with the juice of half a lemon

The Yeast and Yoghurt Diet

When the skin is in poor condition the same can usually be said of the hair and nails. They all benefit noticeably from the following diet, and for flaking nails there is no better cure than this combination of yeast and yoghurt in the diet. At the same time the weight loss is appreciable.

Fresh yeast is not only more rapidly effective than dried yeast but its calorie count is much less:

1 oz (28.35 g) dried yeast = 100c
1 oz (28.35 g) fresh yeast = 25c

It is obtainable at all health food shops and at many bakeries.

Very little bread, 2 slices wholemeal per day.

No cakes or biscuits or sugar.

$\frac{3}{4}$ pint (0.428 litre) skimmed milk per day.

A little butter.

$\frac{1}{3}$ oz (9.45 g) fresh yeast per day.

2 plain yoghurts per day (5 fl. oz or 15 cl each).

1 tablespoon of wheatgerm.

Vegetables, fruit, eggs, unfermented cheese.

Red meat and poultry.

SAMPLE MENUS

On waking up   1 glass of hot water with squeeze of lemon sipped as hot as possible while still in bed

Just before breakfast, a piece of fresh yeast dissolved in a little milk

Breakfast   A large cup of hot skimmed milk flavoured with tea or coffee
1 plain yoghurt and 1 tbs wheatgerm
or
1 slice wholemeal bread, 1 soft-boiled egg

Mid-morning   1 glass of cold water and 1 plain yoghurt with 1 tbs wheatgerm (if not taken at breakfast)

Lunch   2 grilled kidneys
3 tbs broccoli with Lemon Sauce (page 85)
1 slice Edam cheese
1 plain yoghurt
Tea or coffee with skimmed milk

Mid-afternoon   2 glasses of cold water

Dinner   Half an hour before dinner 1 glass of cold water

Mixed green salad with 1 tbs Diet Dressing No. 2 (page 68)
1 slice lean roast beef (no skin or gravy)
or
Small grilled steak
1 small jacket potato (eat the skin) served with 1 tablespoon of cottage cheese or Yoghurt
Half a grilled grapefruit or 1 orange, or a portion of strawberries or raspberries
Large cup of herb tea or Lemon Tisane (page 58)

Before retiring 1 glass of cold water

The Grapefruit Diet

Citrus fruits are catalysts of fats, and the success of the following diet depends on a balanced quantity of both.

No bread, no alcohol, no sugar, a little butter and olive oil.

2 slices of bacon per day.

Plenty of citrus fruit and juices. Tomato juice as a change.

Lean meat, eggs, vegetables and salads.

SAMPLE MENUS

On waking up A glass of hot water with the juice of 1 lemon, sipped as hot as possible while in bed

Breakfast Half a grapefruit
2 scrambled or soft-boiled eggs with 2 slices of lean *grilled* bacon

Tea or coffee with skimmed milk

Mid-morning Large glass of water with juice of 1 lemon or half a grapefruit instead

Lunch Half a grapefruit (grilled for a change)
1 portion grilled steak or liver, brushed on both sides with melted butter and sprinkled with lemon juice

1 portion of french beans
1 portion of Tomato and Cucumber Salad (page 70) with French Dressing (page 69)
Glass of china tea with lemon juice

Mid-afternoon   1 glass cold water with lemon juice

Dinner   Half an hour before dinner a small glass of grapefruit or tomato juice
Half a grapefruit
1 lamb chop or portion of fresh lobster or crab
Portion of spinach or broccoli with Lemon Sauce (page 85)
1 glass of Lemon Tisane with 1 extra teaspoon of juice added (page 58)

Before retiring   1 glass of cold water or skimmed milk

The Health Diet

A nature diet of raw vegetables and fruits can be much more appetising than one would imagine and is well suited to everybody's dietary needs, as well as those who must lose weight Being composed mainly of uncooked foods its vitamin content is maximum, since high temperatures destroy vitamins more rapidly than anything else. This diet has a very vitalising effect.

No sauces, no alcohol, a little wholemeal bread.

A little honey, $1\frac{1}{2}$ tbs of wheatgerm daily.

Plenty of dairy produce, cheese, milk, eggs, a little butter.

Plenty of fruit and vegetables.

A little underdone meat. Fish preferably uncooked and prepared in the Japanese fashion.

SAMPLE MENUS

On waking up   A glass of hot water sipped as hot as possible while still in bed

Breakfast   Raw Oatmeal and Apple Porridge (page 78)

or

2 soft-boiled eggs, 1 slice wholemeal bread
and 1 tsp of honey
Milk hot or cold, half a glass

Mid-morning 2 glasses of cold water

Lunch Half an hour before lunch a small glass
of fresh vegetable juice, i.e. watercress
and carrot, spinach, carrot and onion,
celery and tomato, etc., made in electric
juice-extractor
Portion of Pickled Lemon Fish (page 97)
or Fish Salad (page 99)

or

1 slice Cheshire, cheddar or Dutch cheese
A raw Cabbage Salad or other raw vegetable dish (Chapter 5)
Fresh peaches, apricots or strawberries
in season, or in winter, grapes, apple,
pear or orange

Mid-afternoon 1 glass of half milk and half soda-water

Dinner A glass of cold water half an hour before
dinner
Raw Vegetable Platter (page 75) with
Diet Dressing Nos. 1 or 2 (page 67) and
$1\frac{1}{2}$ tbs of wheatgerm
An artichoke with Lemon Sauce (page
85)
Fresh fruit in season, strawberries, raspberries, red currants with Fromage Blanc
(page 92)
Rose-hip tea

If preferred, the evening meal can be replaced entirely by
an Eggnog, a glassful of skimmed milk warmed to blood
heat with a beaten egg whisked into it and flavoured with
either a teaspoonful of honey and a big pinch of nutmeg
or cinnamon, or a savoury seasoning of coarse-crystal sea
salt and black pepper. If preferred, the milk need not be

heated. This constitutes a complete meal in itself at the total calorie cost of 246c for the sweet version and 232c for the savoury one.

The Balanced Diet

What we all search for, and should have, is the ideal diet which is varied and interesting and can be adapted to our way of living, one that will cater to all our nutritional needs, and from which we will suffer no sense of deprivation. Above all, we long for a diet that will allow us to eat whatever we fancy and yet gain no weight.

The Balanced Diet fulfils all these needs.

It is given below in the form of approximately 1,500 calories per day which will reduce weight safely and gradually if practised until the desired weight is achieved. Then by increasing the calorie count to approximately 2,000 a day portioned out among the foods calculated to give best nutritional value as indicated on page 23, an active person can then maintain this weight permanently.

Weight should be checked regularly twice a week and marked up beside the scales. This will prevent liberties being taken, whether they are taken unconsciously or not.

Calorie counts must always be respected.

This is the favourite diet and permanent way of eating of those smart, slim Frenchwomen one sees in all good restaurants in Paris eating seriously (that is, gastronomically speaking). They have to or they would never be invited again.

For each day's consumption:

Wholemeal bread, $3\frac{1}{2}$ oz (100 g) (freshly baked)	242c
Skimmed milk, $\frac{1}{2}$ Imperial pint (approx. $\frac{1}{4}$ litre or 10 fluid ounces)	100c
Sugar, $\frac{3}{4}$ oz (23.61 g) (better replaced by 1 dessertspoon of honey)	84c
Lemons (2) for seasoning	30c
Fats, in all (this includes $\frac{1}{2}$ oz (14.17 g) of butter)	205c
Fresh yeast, $\frac{1}{2}$ oz (14.17 g)	13c
Mineral oil (liquid paraffin) $\frac{1}{3}$ oz $= 9.45$ g (optional)	nil
	674c

SAMPLE MENUS

On waking up   Either a large cup of weak china tea with a squeeze of lemon juice or a glass of hot water with the juice of half a lemon, sipped as hot as possible while in bed

Breakfast   A cupful of milk either hot or cold flavoured with tea or coffee, or 1 small carton of plain fat-free yoghurt

Mid-morning   2 glasses of cold water at intervals
An apple, a pear or an orange

Lunch

A portion of grilled meat (beef, lamb or liver) $3\frac{1}{2}$ oz (100 g)	301c
Steamed cauliflower 5 oz (141.75 g) with lemon juice, pepper and chopped mint	22c
Port Salut cheese 1 oz (28.35 g)	88c
1 slice fresh pineapple 5 oz (141.75 g)	65c
Black coffee (with honey ration) or tea	nil
	476c

Mid-afternoon   2 glasses of cold water at intervals

Dinner

1 large slice lean boiled ham	137c
Ratatouille (page 87), 5 oz (141.75 g)	73c
Roquefort cheese or Gorgonzola 1 oz (28.35 g)	112c
1 fresh peach, large	52c
Mint or other herb tea	nil
	374c

Before retiring   1 glass of hot water with the juice of half a lemon

This makes a daily calorie count of approximately 1,500c including the mid-morning fruit and the yoghurt if it is taken for breakfast instead of milk. If not, it can be used to make a good sweet course for dinner (see page 91). This number of calories allows a little liberty to be taken on Sundays (but watch it), especially if one day during the week, for beauty's sake, the daily menu is replaced with buttermilk for the entire day. This is delicious and surprisingly sustaining. Buttermilk can be obtained at all the big supermarkets or, if ordered in advance, will be delivered by the milkman.

Providing the calories are counted this excellent diet can be as varied as desired, even to include sausage and mash in controlled quantity, should the craving be irresistible.

The Frenchman's equivalent is Boudin Grillé (grilled black pudding) and the following menu, with many others, gives an idea of what varied and interesting menus are in store for those who live on the Balanced Diet.

Lunch

Grilled Black Pudding and Apple (page 104) (3 large slanting slices cut ½-inch thick) 3 oz (85 g)	246c
2 slices apple 1 oz (28.35 g)	11c
1 jacket potato (eat the skin) served with	90c
1 tablespoon Diet Dressing No. 2	10c
Half a grapefruit	22c
	379c

The following selection of Balanced Diet menus for lunch and dinner and all of them within the permitted calorie count will, I hope, solve the problems many dieting housewives have to face when catering for a family of which the other members are not dieting. The difference is bridged by adding a potato dish, and substituting a pudding for the fruit and cheese eaten by dieters, which, by the way, are much more nutritious than the pudding.

Balanced Diet Menus

Portion Raw Mushroom Salad (page 69) with French Dressing
Veal chop (meat only), 3½ oz (100 g) approx. (grilled with a little butter, lemon and herbs)
Braised chicory, 3½ oz (100 g)

Gorgonzola or Stilton cheese, $\frac{1}{2}$ oz (14.175 g)
Grapes
Coffee, Mint or Lemon Tea

Winter Salad (page 73), $3\frac{1}{2}$ oz (100 g)
Fish Salad or Fish Pie (page 101), 5 oz (113.4 g)
Brussels Sprouts and Apple (page 84), $3\frac{1}{2}$ oz (100 g)
3 fresh apricots

Portion of Summer Vegetables (page 83)
Omelette (2 eggs) with mushrooms, 2 oz (56.7 g)
1 heart lettuce with Dressing Nos 1 or 2 (page 67)
1 pear and 1 orange, medium size
Coffee

6–8 radishes and a heart of raw celery
Roast lamb, 2 small medium thick slices, $3\frac{1}{2}$ oz (100 g) (no fat, skin or gravy)
French beans, 5 oz (145.74 g) (served with half day's butter ration and chopped parsley)
1 baked banana (page 94)

Roast chicken breast, $3\frac{1}{2}$ oz (100 g) (no skin or gravy)
Baked courgettes (small green Zucchini), $3\frac{1}{2}$ oz (100 g)
Leaf spinach, $3\frac{1}{2}$ oz (100 g) (served with half daily butter ration and lemon juice)
1 slice Cheshire cheese, 1 oz (28.35 g)
Fresh cherries, 5 oz (141.74 g) or a portion Orange and Apple Cream (page 92)

$\frac{1}{2}$ Grilled Poussin with Lemon and Garlic (page 105)
Watercress and Spinach Salad (page 70), $3\frac{1}{2}$ oz (100 g)
Portion of Danish Blue cheese, 1 oz (28.35 g)
Compôte of fresh apricots or peaches, 5 oz (141.74 g) (page 93), served with $1\frac{1}{2}$ tbs wheatgerm

Portion Ratatouille (page 87) with poached egg
Cottage cheese $2\frac{1}{2}$ oz (42.52 g) flavoured with soy sauce and chives
Coffee or tea with skimmed milk of daily ration

Portion of Spring Appetiser (page 77)
2 grilled kidneys, $3\frac{1}{2}$ oz (approx. 100 g)
2 grilled tomatoes, medium size

Strawberries or raspberries, 5 oz (141.74 g)
Glass of skimmed milk and soda

Portion of Italian Spinach Salad, 3½ oz (100 g)
Baked Fish with Herbs, 6 oz (170 g) (page 98)
Vegetable Charlotte, 3½ oz (100 g) (page 82)
Portion of Bacchante's Cream (page 93)

Baked Beetroot, 3½ oz (100 g) (page 86)
Steak Tartare, 4 oz (113.4 g) (page 103) served with a firm
heart of lettuce and 6 carrot sticks
Raspberries or strawberries, 6 oz (170 g) served with
Fromage Blanc (page 92)

Portion of Lettuce, Spinach and Watercress salad (page 70)
with French Dressing.
2 Eggs Soubise (page 88)
Portion of Mandarin Sorbet (page 94)

Celeriac Salad, 3½ oz (100 g) (page 75)
Grilled sweetbreads, 3½ oz (100 g)
Kidney Beans and Onion, 3½ oz (100 g) (page 83)
Cherries or apricots, fresh, 5 oz (141.74 g)

Portion of Vegetable Mould, 3½ oz (100 g) (page 88)
Cold ham and tongue, 3½ oz (100 g)
1 jacket potato medium size served with 1 tbs Yoghurt
1 baked apple

Occasionally a day on a completely vegetarian diet fits
well into the Balanced Diet programme as follows:

SAMPLE MENU

On waking up   A glass of hot water and lemon juice as
usual

Breakfast   A breakfast cup of warm milk and 1 slice
of wholewheat toast with honey and butter
from the daily ration

Mid-morning   A large cupful of hot Beauty Broth (page
107) and later a glass of cold water

Lunch Portion of Cucumber Appetiser served with wheatgerm (page 77)
Mushrooms cooked in remains of daily fats ration with chopped parsley and lemon juice, 4 oz (113.4 g)
Baked Beetroot (page 86)
1 large apple or pear

Mid-afternoon 1 glass of cold water with lemon juice and later 1 individual carton plain yoghurt with 1 tbs wheatgerm.

Dinner 2 hearts of artichokes with Devilled Cheese (tomatoes or mushrooms can be used instead) (page 86)
Portion of Vegetable Casserole (page 81)
1 large orange

After lunch, coffee and tea can be replaced on vegetarian days with one of the various herb teas. By drinking camomile tea with orange flower water instead of coffee after dinner, a sound night's sleep is assured.

Chapter 4

Diet Cooking Recommendations

When the western world was swept some years ago by the mania for food fit to make a gourmet out of Everyman, there swept with it a belief that good food is complicated food, rich, costly and dependent on wine and cream for its goodness. This is not so.

Good food is the result of ingredients of good quality carefully cooked and correctly seasoned. These elements can be combined to produce diet food just as appetising as any dinner party food.

It is the seasoning which can turn the simplest dish into a notable one. By seasoning I do not mean the indiscriminate use of herbs scattered over the main ingredient in such a variety that the original flavour disappears beneath them, and I certainly do not mean using quantities of salt. The savour of good food does not need salt to emphasise it. Many excellent dishes can be prepared entirely without it. While carrying no calorie count, salt, that is refined table salt, should be used sparingly. Coarse sea salt is preferable by far from a general health point of view.

The abuse of salt is common to the majority of European people, according to statistics, possibly because their taste buds are jaded by smoking, possibly because they ignore the fact that the use of too much salt contributes more than any other condiment to hardening of the arteries – another name for old age.

While a certain amount of salt is essential for the correct functioning of the body, it is dispensed with entirely in certain diets. Entirely is, however, a relative term since many of the foods we all eat currently, whether on a diet or not, provide an ample supply of salt naturally; foods such as wholewheat bread, ryecrisp biscuits, butter, non-fermented yellow cheeses like Cheddar, Cheshire, Dutch Edam, also greens, turnips, fish and bananas.

In those diets where salt is excluded, as for example in the Young Mother's Diet, this is advised because excess salt causes liquids to be retained in the body instead of allowing them to pass quickly through the body carrying toxic wastes with them. All the more reason for cutting down on salt for the duration of any diet.

In the case of completely salt-free diets extra vitamins are usually prescribed to compensate, and foods rich in iron (apricots, eggs, sweetbreads, liver and other offal) and potassium (meat, fish, olives, dried fruit, almonds) are recommended.

The peasants of Southern Italy, who live to a ripe old age and work hard until the end of it, are a notable exception to this European convention of salt-abusers. They are a spare wiry race of people who attribute their longevity to the fact that they use very little salt indeed. Being a state monopoly, salt is too expensive for them to use currently, and so they replace it by seasoning their food with the one commodity which can be obtained in their part of the country for the picking – lemons. They sprinkle lemon juice on meat and fish before it is either grilled or baked, on vegetables both hot and cold, as well as using it to dress the green salad which is a fixed item of their staple diet.

Lemon in all its forms, juice, pulp and peel, is a valuable source of vitamin C which builds up one's fund of physical energy and thus protects against fatigue. Hence the athletes' habit of sucking half a lemon at frequent intervals.

Lemons for those on a diet take the place of many seasonings, and the absence of salt on a salt-free diet is not noticed when lemon juice is substituted for it. It is an important ingredient in many diet dressings and dishes which are good enough to be presented at a dinner party. Used instead of vinegar in salad dressings, lemon juice renders the salad more digestible as well as making the addition of salt unnecessary. Mayonnaise (yes! there is a diet mayonnaise) is given piquancy by adding a few drops of lemon juice as a final touch. Added to the water in which rice is boiled, a tablespoonful of lemon juice will prevent the grains from sticking together and keep it white. When making a parsley sauce a little lemon juice will make a great improvement to the flavour.

The peel of a lemon, either fresh or dried, makes an after-dinner infusion which is both digestive and refreshing to take in place of coffee. This Lemon-peel Tisane is very decorative if the peel is removed from the fruit in one long thin spiral, put into a china cup with a little lemon juice and covered with boiling water. If left to infuse for just a minute the resulting drink is delicious, even without sugar. The Italians in certain regions call this a Canarino – a little canary – and drink it frequently, especially after a rich meal.

As another delicious infusion to take in place of the sugar and milkless tea or coffee recommended on all diets but so difficult for some people to get used to, I do advise Mint Tea. This is made with either fresh garden mint in season, or in winter with dried mint bought loose at all herbalists and health food shops. Keep a special little china teapot to make it in, and use 2 teaspoonsful of chopped fresh mint for 2 teacups of boiling water, or 1 heaped teaspoonful of the dried variety. There are many kinds of herb tea to use, lime-flower, camomile, rose-hip, etc., etc., and when a teaspoonful of orange-flower water is added to a cupful of camomile tea, a deliciously subtle flavour results.

Condiments generally can be replaced to advantage by fresh chopped herbs. Chopped parsley, mint, tarragon or fennel can add a subtle flavour to a green salad or dish of cooked vegetables while providing an added source of vitamins and valuable minerals. The tender green leaves of radishes are an interesting addition to a lettuce salad, and they too are high in mineral content. A big pinch of dried marjoram added to scrambled eggs or an omelette makes other seasoning unnecessary.

Freshly ground black pepper, preferably the large black pimento corns, make the absence of salt unnoticeable; these Jamaican pimento corns are much more aromatic than the ordinary black pepper corns, and give a very distinctive flavour to a French Dressing.

The stress on the use of salads in diet menus has a two-fold purpose. One is that salad greens help the absorption of fats, and the second is that their calorie count being very low, a fair quantity can be eaten and this helps to give a satisfied feeling. Because of this it is a good plan to start a diet meal with a salad of some kind, either green or made of raw vegetables.

For the many people who regard salads as the last gastronomic resource, a very savoury dressing, high in vitamin content and low in calorie count, goes a long way towards changing their opinion. With these dieters in mind I have evolved over the years several different dressings which can be used over raw or cooked vegetables to make a very savoury luncheon dish, or to give an extra fillip to the usual green salad. The recipes for them are given in Chapter 5.

When normal weight is regained and the Balanced Diet adopted as a regular way of eating, the cleansing of the whole bodily system from which the dieter has benefited, reveals itself in a much sharper appreciation of flavours. One is struck, for example, by the tastelessness of white bread, unless one is sufficiently lucky to have tracked down an individual bakery where hand-made oven-baked bread is made from good strong flour. But wholewheat bread has much more flavour than any white bread. Not that whole-wheat bread counts for less calories, they remain the same as those of white bread, but wholewheat flour retains a far greater proportion of the vitamins and minerals which the over-refining of white flour reduces drastically.

Making one's own bread is a laborious process for which few of us now have the time, no matter how fascinating it may be to the dedicated cook, but the wholewheat flour bread-mix sold in all health food shops is very simply and quickly made into a beautiful loaf. By just mixing the suggested quantity of cold water into the prepared flour and baking it in a hot oven for 40 minutes one can make delicious bread and this constitutes an admirable stand-by. It is also very long-keeping, remaining fresh for over a week.

The skimmed milk recommended for so many diets is

now obtainable from most chain dairies and will be delivered on request, but to produce it oneself in an emergency is no great chore. Likewise when large quantities of yoghurt are eaten it is much more economical to make this oneself, and instructions and recipes for making both of these diet requirements, along with all the other suggested dishes, are given in the following chapters.

Grilling (the method of cooking ingredients one side at a time *underneath* the source of heat, and known to Americans as broiling), as opposed to frying, is the way of cooking meat and fish recommended not only for dieters, but for anyone who has respect for his stomach and what he puts into it; grilling makes protein more easily digestible, liquefies and drains away the natural fats from the ingredients cooked and if correctly done gives very tender results.

The object of grilling is to seal the surface of the meat or fish as quickly as possible at a high temperature so that the natural juices are retained. This is why meat should never be pierced with a fork in order to turn it, but picked up with a pair of cooking tongs. In order to seal meat correctly, the grill should be heated at maximum temperature for at least 3 minutes before the prepared food is placed under it.

Steak should be grilled at maximum temperature close to the grill for 4 minutes, turned over and grilled for a further 4 minutes, no more. Eight minutes in all is ample time to cook a steak $\frac{3}{4}$ inch thick. A thicker one will require slightly longer cooking at reduced temperature.

Placing the food under a grill which has not been thoroughly pre-heated to a high sharp temperature, but which has the heat turned on as the food is placed under it. means that as the heat slowly increases the juices are drawn out of the meat, which then becomes dry, tough and tasteless.

Lamb chops and cutlets and mutton chops, after being sealed at high temperature for 2 minutes, require longer cooking with the temperature reduced, to liquefy and drain away the much higher fat content.

Liver is one of the best protein foods we have, especially pig's liver. Lamb's, beef and chicken livers come next in the scale of values, and the expensive calf's liver we prize so highly counts less than we think it does, having been boosted into exclusiveness by demand.

Liver of one kind or another should be served at least once a week. It should be very lightly cooked, more by the heat of the pan itself than the heat under it. Whether a non-stick surfaced pan which requires no fat is used, or the heirloom iron frying pan, the method is the same.

Heat a thick heavy frying pan over moderate heat for several minutes, with nothing in it at all, then put in half a teaspoonful of butter from the daily ration, and as soon as this froths seal the slice of liver in it for 1 minute on each side. Then reduce the heat to the absolute minimum, cover the pan and leave the meat until it is soft but cooked through and still pink inside. This should take about 2 minutes after sealing for a slice of liver $\frac{1}{4}$ inch thick.

Though gravy *per se* is forbidden on a reducing diet as an unwanted additive of meat fats and flour, the permitted amount of butter in which the liver was cooked and the juices left in the pan can be combined and poured over the meat in the following way. Working very rapidly because liver continues cooking by its own heat after being taken from the pan, remove the lid after the first minute of cooking, add 1 teaspoon of wine vinegar (either tarragon or garlic flavoured) mixed with 1 tablespoon of warm water for each half-teaspoon of butter used. Mix the juices and diluted vinegar well together, remove the liver to a heated serving dish and as soon as the liquids bubble pour them over the meat and serve immediately.

Another method is to brush each slice lightly with oil, sprinkle with paprika (which browns it quickly) and grill 1 minute each side.

Sweetbreads can be cooked in this same way after having been washed quickly under cold running water and their membrane gently pulled off, then well dried on a soft kitchen towel.

If salt is used it must never be sprinkled on meat before grilling. This draws the natural juices out of food and with them the mineral content. Grilled meat of any kind can be sprinkled with lemon juice before being cooked, and afterwards. In fact, if done well in advance this helps to make it tender. When using salt it should be sprinkled lightly over the meat when it is taken from under the grill and is about to be served. Marine salt and freshly ground black pepper sprinkled over steak or chops as they are put on the serving dish do not destroy the vitamins or impair the taste.

Fish which are grilled whole like sole, plaice, herrings, etc., should of course be grilled on both sides, steaks of turbot and halibut too, but fillets of sole and other flat fish need only be grilled on one side. All fish is delicious when simply sprinkled with lemon juice and paprika before being grilled and sprinkled with finely chopped parsley as it is served.

Vegetables should *never be left soaking in water, never be over-cooked and never seasoned until they are ready to be served.* Adding salt during the cooking makes them tough and draws their natural properties out into the cooking water, which is then thrown away. If vegetables are cooked in water, seasoning should be added after they are drained. Take a tip from the French housewife, keep the water to add to soup, stock or sauces, and always have fresh chopped herbs handy to sprinkle on top. Better still, follow the method given in Chapter 6 for cooking vegetables without any water at all. It makes them deliciously full of flavour and worthy of being served as a separate course.

All food should be as lightly and quickly cooked as possible for maximum benefit to be derived from it. Long cooking at high temperature destroys vitamins and minerals, and any food cooked for too long in an open vessel becomes difficult to digest and devoid of nutritional value. The long slow cooking of casserole dishes makes the ingredients tender and digestible, but also draws out the juices from the food into the sauce or gravy. This does, however, form an important part of the dish and benefit is derived from the sauce more than from the meat and vegetables in it.

No food should be over-cooked, meat especially. Beef should be cooked medium rare at most, under-done preferably. Lamb should be cooked to no more than medium point for full flavour and nutritional value. This is not the English custom, but it should carve into rosy-pink slices and this, when cold, is delicious. Liver of all kinds should be very lightly cooked and served pink inside; only pork should be well-cooked, and that, the slower the better.

After sealing, all meat should be baked at a low temperature. All vegetables, except potatoes, should be cooked until only just tender and retain, when served, their crisp, quality.

Boiled eggs should not be boiled, but placed in a panful of boiling water, covered, and left removed from the direct source of heat for 8 minutes. A very fresh egg, say up to 3 days old, will need 10 minutes. Cooked in this way they will be found set, soft and easily digestible.

While fast-reducing diets (the H.P. Diet and the Astronaut's Diet) insist on the elimination of all fats until normal weight is regained, the Balanced Diet, which must then be resumed, insists that a certain amount of fats be included.

The human body needs fats for their vitamin content which keep the nervous system, the skin and hair in good condition. The irritability of people who remain endlessly on a fat-free diet out of vanity, proves this. While non-saturated fats such as corn, wheatgerm, safflower oil and vegetable-oil margarines are recommended by doctors to some patients, there is no reason why normal healthy dieters should not enjoy good butter and olive oil, in limited quantities, both for their flavour and their vitamin content as well. The calorie count is the same.

So choose first grade butter which is well flavoured and enjoy the quantity allowed in the daily calorie count, using it either in the natural state or to enhance the flavour of vegetables, or grilled meat and fish. Choose the best quality olive oil, preferably the one which comes from the first pressing of the olive. It is greenish in colour, very perfumed, and highly flavoured, which makes a little go a long way.

In parenthesis, and from the superb to the acceptable, there is one edible oil which carries no calorie count at all, and that is mineral oil. This odourless, colourless oil which we in England commonly call liquid paraffin, makes a good salad dressing when combined with flavoured wine vinegar and fresh herbs. It is well suited to the dieter's purpose, since it also provides the necessary lubrication to correct a tendency to constipation which a radical change of diet can occasion in some people. For this reason it is recommended by several well-known French diet specialists. Other doctors, both European and American, disagree with its use even for a limited diet period. Its use is a matter of opinion.

The choice of oil for frying need not be discussed, since fried food, whether on a diet or not, is neither a healthy form of cooking nor one practised by the good cooks of this world except for isolated dishes like Pommes Lyonnaises or Beignets.

The disadvantage of fried foods, from a health point of view, is that in order to fry ingredients to the required state of crisp dryness, any cooking fat must be brought to such a high temperature that it decomposes into highly indigestible particles; the higher the temperature the more indigestible the food.

It is interesting to note therefore that the decomposition temperatures for both butter and olive oil are considerably less than those of lard and the so-called frying oils:

406°Fahrenheit (208 °Centigrade) for butter, *347°F* (175 °C) for olive oil as opposed to *432°F* (222 °C) and up to *450°F* (232 °C) for corn and other frying oils. The various types of lard also have high decomposition figures, from *417°F* (214 °C) to *430°F* (221 °C).

The reason for choosing good butter and fine olive oil is evident both from a gastronomic and health point of view.

Quality should never be sacrificed, especially on a diet. Good well-flavoured food helps to eradicate that feeling of privation from which most dieters suffer. Also the knowledge that you can have anything you fancy eating (provided that the calorie count is respected) will automatically still a dieter's craving – so will eating it slowly, chewing it thoroughly and savouring the flavour to the full while doing so.

Chapter 5

Diet Dressings, Salads and Raw Vegetables

Well-flavoured dressings are essential to the success of any salad. Diet dressings are especially important since they must be not too high in calorie cost and yet be a savoury addition to the vegetable ingredients.

Here are several new and different ones which can be used in a variety of dishes, and they are guaranteed to make a confirmed salad enthusiast out of the most dedicated meat-and-potato man.

The first dressing has no calorie count at all, and for those whose diet allows a small quantity of mineral oil (liquid paraffin) it is indistinguishable from a French Dressing made with corn oil, when flavoured with wine vinegar and fresh herbs.

The given quantity will dress a green salad for four people.

L. P. DRESSING

2 tablespoons mineral oil (liquid paraffin)
1 tablespoon tarragon, garlic or other wine vinegar freshly ground Jamaican pimento corns

1 saltspoon sea salt (coarse crystals)
1 tablespoon chopped fresh tarragon or mint in season (parsley or green tops of young onions can be used in winter)

Grind the sea salt into the salad bowl and add the vinegar. Beat this well until the salt is dissolved and then add the oil drop by drop beating constantly with a fork. When the dressing is thick and cloudy add sufficient freshly ground pepper to season well, and last of all the herbs. This dressing must be very well beaten.

The addition of a fresh egg yolk will make an extra-special dressing at the calorie cost of 61c for the yolk. To do this mix the yolk well with three or four drops of vinegar and a big pinch of salt, in a large bowl and add the dressing, already mixed and well beaten, drop by drop into the egg yolk. This salad dressing is suitable for all green leaf and raw vegetable salads but it should not be used with hot ingredients.

A very good mayonnaise which can be served with cold turbot or halibut is made with similar ingredients.

L. P. MAYONNAISE (serves 4)

1 large egg yolk
4 tablespoons mineral oil
(liquid paraffin)
1 saltspoon ground sea salt
¼ saltspoon ground
Jamaican pimento corns

1½ teaspoons wine vinegar
(tarragon, Orleans or garlic)
1 teaspoon lemon juice
1 tablespoon chopped fresh
herbs (tarragon, mint or
chives)

Put the egg yolk into the bottom of a large soup plate (this makes the mayonnaise set more easily than when made in a deep bowl). Add the salt and three or four drops of the vinegar. Mix well with a wooden spoon or spatula before starting to add the oil drop by drop, stirring it in wide circles round the plate. Set the plate on a damp cloth if it slides about during this operation. When all the oil is mixed in and the mayonnaise thick and creamy, add the rest of the vinegar drop by drop, still stirring, and then the lemon juice. Last of all add pepper to taste and the chopped herbs. If necessary add a little more lemon juice.

Remoulade, that very piquant dressing used in celeriac salad (page 75), is made at the very low calorie cost of 18c per person in the following way.

REMOULADE (serves 4)

L.P. Mayonnaise as above
1 teaspoon capers

2 small pickled gherkins
ground black pepper

Make the mayonnaise as previously indicated. Drain the capers and the gherkins on a piece of kitchen paper and chop them very small, mix them into the mayonnaise and add more seasoning if required. Chill before serving. Note: When L.P. Dressing is used the daily quantity of mineral oil indicated on the Balanced Diet may be omitted.

To make the following low calorie dressing it is essential to use the type of skimmed-milk cheese known as cottage or curd cheese. It is sold unflavoured, in bulk in delicatessen shops and the food halls of the big department stores, and is the cheapest of this variety of cheese. The kind processed into little pellets and sold in cartons is not suitable for this use nor is the more expensive one known as cream cheese, which in any case is made from whole milk and therefore does not make a dressing low in calories.

DIET DRESSING NO. 1 (serves 1)

1 tablespoon cottage (curd) cheese
2 tablespoons skimmed milk
1 dessertspoon tarragon vinegar or lemon juice

1 teaspoon soy sauce
black pepper
1 teaspoon finely grated onion or chopped chives (optional)

Beat the skimmed milk into the cottage cheese until a thick cream is obtained. Next add the soy sauce, the pepper and the tarragon vinegar, beating them all in, to dilute the dressing to a smooth flowing cream. If preferred the milk can be omitted and a mixture of tarragon vinegar and water used instead. Add the grated onion or chopped chives last of all. This is an excellent dressing to use either on a green salad or a salad of raw or cooked vegetables. In the latter case mixing the dressing into the vegetables while they are still warm from the pan will give the finished dish a much more definite flavour than if the dressing is added when they are cold. Calorie count, 17c per portion.

The flavour of the yoghurt used in the next dressing is disguised by the other ingredients used, and this is useful in preparing salads for dieters who claim not to like yoghurt. Its aperient value is important for people who are affected by the change-over of eating habits when first starting a diet.

DIET DRESSING NO. 2 (serves 1)

2 tablespoons plain yoghurt
1 dessertspoon soy sauce
freshly ground pepper to
taste

1 tablespoon chopped fresh
herbs in season (tarragon,
chives, mint or parsley)

Beat the soy sauce into the yoghurt and add pepper to taste. Mix in the chopped herbs beating well to incorporate them. Chill until ready to use. A few drops of lemon juice can be added if a sharper dressing is required.

Calorie count, 35c per portion. The quantities given for both Diet Dressings Nos 1 and 2 are for one person since they can both be used to prepare a quickly made snack meal.

A good French Dressing combines well with all salad materials, both the leafy green kinds and raw or cooked root vegetables. Again in the case of a salad made of cooked vegetables the dressing should be added while they are still hot from the pan, so that they absorb the flavours both of the olive oil and the fresh herbs. This is why good oil, either French, Italian or Spanish, should be used, and not the anonymous pale tasteless kind sold in drug stores, as many of our newest chemists shops are now called after the American fashion. The fruity flavour of the olive is essential to a good dressing, as it is to many other excellent vegetable dishes.

The preparation of a green salad is an art in itself, and if I devote space to this operation at the end of this chapter it is only because the sight of a bowlful of limp, soggy lettuce and the taste of a sharp vinegary dressing are enough to ruin any meal. A well-flavoured *crisp* salad is always a welcome item on the menu appreciated for its cleansing effect on the palate after a rich main course, and also for its digestive effect. On a diet, it supplies essential nutritional needs . . . and that piquant flavour we crave.

FRENCH DRESSING (serves 4)

3 dessertspoons olive oil	*freshly ground black pepper*
1 dessertspoon wine vinegar	*1 tablespoon chopped fresh*
(or lemon juice)	*parsley or chives*
½ teaspoon coarse salt	

Put the salt into the salad bowl and beat the lemon juice into it until dissolved, then add the oil, beating constantly until the mixture is cloudy before adding the herbs It is important to beat the mixture well otherwise the oil is not blended properly with the lemon juice or vinegar and the dressing will be sharp and acid instead of being piquant. Calorie count, 70c per portion.

Green salad, even when well prepared, if dressed too early becomes limp. If the salad for a dinner party, for example, must be made in advance, make the dressing in a big bowl, cross the wooden salad fork and spoon (never metal) in the bottom of it, and pile the prepared leaves of lettuce, endive, watercress, batavia, etc., on top of them so that they do not touch the dressing. Place in the refrigerator and turn the leaves over once or twice very carefully during the waiting time. In this way they will dry completely and keep crisp for two hours or more. Turn the salad over and over very lightly to coat with the dressing, but only at the moment of serving.

When practising the Balanced Diet one can make many other delicious dishes with French Dressing for an appetising first or main course.

MUSHROOM SALAD (serves 4)

8 oz (226.8 g) small	*4 dessertspoons French or*
mushrooms	*L.P. Dressing*
1 tablespoon lemon juice	*A little paprika*

Either wash and dry the mushrooms or peel them, never both. Scrape and trim the stalks and cut the mushrooms, stalks as well, into slices the thickness of a 10p piece. Place in the serving dish and sprinkle immediately with lemon juice to prevent discoloration. Beat the dressing thoroughly and pour it over the sliced mushrooms. Turn them over and over to take the dressing and sprinkle liberally with paprika before serving.

A variation of this salad is to cook the prepared mushrooms in a dessertspoon of lemon juice and 3 tablespoons of water in a covered pan for 10 minutes. Then drain well and pat dry on kitchen paper before dressing them, while still warm, with either French or No. 2 Diet Dressing and plenty of chopped parsley. Chill before serving.

The liquor made during the cooking should be reserved and added to the Chicken Broth for which the recipe is given later.

Calorie count 74c per portion, made with French Dressing, and 39c made with Diet Dressing No. 2.

LETTUCE, SPINACH AND WATERCRESS SALAD (serves 4)

Half a large firm heart of lettuce
1 handful of young spinach

1 bunch watercress
4 dessertspoons of French Dressing

Prepare the salad as indicated at the end of the chapter then separate the lettuce leaves, pick the ribs from the spinach and the tougher stems from the watercress before leaving it all to crisp. When required, tear the salad into pieces, place them in a large bowl and toss lightly in the dressing until evenly coated. Calorie count, 77c per portion.

In winter when lettuce is scarce and tasteless into the bargain a Tomato and Cucumber Salad can be very acceptable to the dieter because it is filling.

TOMATO AND CUCUMBER SALAD (serves 4)

4 large tomatoes
half a cucumber
4 young green onions

4 dessertspoons French Dressing
1 tablespoon chopped parsley

Buy the Spanish tomatoes if possible, they are meaty and full of flavour hence the reason why they are known in America as Beefsteak tomatoes. Prick each one with a kitchen fork once or twice and hold it over a high gas flame until the skin pops, then peel it. If you cook by electricity, after pricking the tomatoes place them in a wide shallow dish and pour boiling water over them. As soon as they are covered, pour the water off and fill the dish with cold water. This will make the skins peel off easily without softening them. Cut them into slices. Wipe the cucumber with a damp cloth and score the skin from top to bottom with the tines of a fork. Cut into thin slices and arrange them in a long dish alternating with slices of tomatoes. Season with black pepper and coarse salt and pour the dressing over. Leave for one hour before serving, basting the salad occasionally by tipping the dish to one side and scooping up the dressing with a big kitchen spoon to pour it back over the ingredients. Chill slightly and scatter the chopped onions (green stalks as well) and the parsley over the top before serving. Calorie count, 84c per portion.

Garlic can be used instead of young green onions as a flavouring, but do not use more than a cut clove of garlic well rubbed around the inside of the serving dish before the vegetables are arranged in it. Don't crush the clove and add it to the dressing. This way it will kill all other flavours and perhaps an incipient love-affair as well.

Few people eat leeks raw, and they deserve a trial in the following delicious salad.

LEEK SALAD (serves 4)

6 medium sized leeks
2 tablespoons chopped fresh
mint

4 dessertspoons French
Dressing
salt and black pepper
watercress for garnishing

Choose the leeks very fresh so that they will be tender, and cut off all the dark green part of the leaves and the root end leaving only the white and very pale green parts. Remove the outer leaf and slice the leeks into very fine rings. Arrange in the serving dish, beat the chopped mint into the French Dressing and pour it over the leeks. Sprinkle with a little extra salt and pepper, mix well and serve decorated with sprigs of watercress. Calorie count, 80c per portion.

An unusual combination of flavours is found in this luncheon dish.

FENNEL AND MANDARINE SALAD (serves 4)

1 large bulb fresh fennel
4 seedless mandarines
1 teaspoon chopped mint
4 tablespoons L.P. Dressing made with garlic vinegar and no herbs

coarse crystal salt and black pepper
8 radishes
2 hard-boiled eggs

Remove the outside stick of the fennel, which might be discoloured and tough, and cut a slice from the root end. Trim off the cut stems and any of the feathery top leaves which may be faded and cut the bulb in two. Place the cut side on the board and slice as thinly as possible. Arrange in the serving dish in layers sprinkling each one with salt and pepper and a little of the dressing into which the finely chopped mint has been beaten. Only use half the dressing, reserve the rest. Leave the fennel to marinate for one hour. Peel the mandarines, scrape off the white pith and cut into thin slices. Arrange them on top of the fennel alternated with rings of hard-boiled egg, season and pour the remainder of the dressing over the whole. Garnish with radishes trimmed into rosettes. To do this remove the leaves and slice the skin downwards into petals without severing them. When the radishes are placed in a little iced water in the refrigerator the petals will curl back to form rosettes. Calorie count, 52c per portion.

If you like raw onions and are on the Balanced Diet, use your slices of wholemeal bread one day to make this very savoury combination.

ONION AND CUCUMBER SALAD (serves 4)

3 medium sized purple-skinned onions
half a cucumber
2 slices stale wholemeal bread

4 dessertspoons L.P. or French Dressing
1 tablespoon chopped parsley
coarse sea salt
black pepper

This salad is best made with the purple-skinned onions which are sweet and mild in flavour. Skin them before slicing into thin rings, then skin and slice the cucumber thinly. Rub the bread into fine crumbs and put a layer in the bottom of the salad bowl. Add a layer of onions, another of breadcrumbs, then a layer of cucumber and more breadcrumbs, and so on until the ingredients are used, sprinkling each layer of vegetables with a little coarse salt and black pepper. Cover the bowl and refrigerate for one hour until cold. Pour the dressing over the contents half an hour before serving and garnish with chopped parsley. Toss thoroughly at the moment of serving. Calorie count, 112c per portion with French Dressing.

When salad materials of all kinds are very expensive a good winter salad can be made with the heart of white cabbage, with other raw vegetables added to give interest to both colour and flavour. The vitamin C content of this salad is high.

WINTER SALAD (serves 4)

8 oz (226.8 g) firm white cabbage
¼ sweet red pepper
1 Cox's apple (large)
(or any hard crisp eating apple, e.g. Green Pippin)

¼ small Spanish onion
1 bunch watercress
1 tablespoon chopped parlsey
4 tablespoons L.P. Dressing
freshly milled black pepper

Cut the pepper in two halves lengthways, wash the seeds out under running water, dry well and cut out the inner membrane and the stalk end, and then slice the pepper into long thin strips. Peel and slice the onion into very thin rings. Wash and pick over the watercress adding the chopped stalks to the salad and reserving the sprigs of leaves. Shred the cabbage as finely as possible, and starting with this fill a large salad bowl with layers . . . shredded cabbage, parsley, seasoning and a little dressing, onion, grated unpeeled apple, red pepper, watercress stalks, more dressing and so on until the bowl is full. Then mix very thoroughly indeed turning the ingredients over and over with a wooden spoon and fork. Cover the bowl with a plate and leave for at least 2 hours before serving. When required, decorate with the sprigs of watercress and serve. The calorie count of each serving of Winter Salad is 49c. If an egg yolk is added to the dressing the calorie count becomes 64c.

Another satisfying main course salad and one with an appetising flavour is:

BEER AND CABBAGE SALAD (serves 4)

8 oz (226.8 g) firm white cabbage
1 green pepper
2 heaped tablespoons cottage cheese
half a breakfastcup of beer
¼ teaspoon ground crystal salt

¼ teaspoon black pepper
A big pinch of white pepper
2 tablespoons celery seed (or caraway seed may be substituted)
1 teaspoon grated onion

Wash the cabbage quickly under running water, dry it and remove the outer leaves, and cut a thick slice from the root end. Slice into quarters, remove the centre rib and cut the cabbage into fine shreds. Beat the beer, ground crystal salt and pepper into the cottage cheese to obtain a thin cream, mix in the celery seed, add the grated onion and test for seasoning. This dressing requires more pepper than most. Arrange the shredded cabbage in layers in a large bowl covering each one with the dressing. Mix the ingredients well together before covering the bowl and leaving the salad to marinate for 2 hours before serving. Calorie count, 62c per portion.

Simple but unusually flavoured is this salad made with raw cauliflower.

CAULIFLOWER MINT SALAD (serves 4)

1 medium sized cauliflower
2 tablespoons fresh chopped mint

4 portions Diet Dressing No. 1
salt and black pepper
paprika

Remove all the outer leaves and the root end of the cauliflower and plunge it up and down very quickly several times in cold water. Shake free of moisture, dry it and then break it up into small florets. Chop these into small pieces. Put the curd dressing into a large bowl which will enable the contents to be turned over easily, and mix in the chopped mint. Add the prepared cauliflower, season and mix well. Test for seasoning and add more black pepper if necessary. Chill for one hour and sprinkle the surface of the salad with paprika before serving. This salad can also be made with raw broccoli heads and the tender part of the stems. Calorie count, 46c per portion.

The Remoulade Dressing given at the beginning of this chapter is used to make:

CELERIE REMOULADE (Celeriac Salad) (serves 4)

half a celeriac root
2 tablespoons lemon juice
Remoulade Dressing
(page 66)

salt (optional) and black pepper

Choose a root on the small side, half of which when peeled and trimmed will give the right quantity (the rest can be cooked in tarragon vinegar-flavoured water and mashed to serve as a hot vegetable). Having peeled the root cut it into very thin slices and then cut these slices into exceedingly fine strips. Put them at once into a shallow dish with the lemon juice to prevent discoloration. Prepare the Remoulade according to the recipe on page 66 while the celeriac softens a little in the lemon juice, then strain this off, pat the vegetable dry on kitchen paper and add it to the sauce. Season and mix well. Test for seasoning and add more pepper if needed. Cover and leave for at least two hours before serving. This salad is even better when prepared the day before it is to be eaten. Calorie count, 43c per portion. When Celeriac Salad is made with Diet Dressing No. 1 the calorie count is 60c per portion.

In the Spring when the new vegetables are at their best an entire meal (and a very beautiful looking one) can be made from a classic French dish looked forward to by all, whether dieting or not.

PLAT DE CRUDITÉS (Raw Vegetable Platter)

cauliflower
carrots
radishes (both red and black)
courgettes (small green zucchini)

green and sweet red peppers
spring onions
celery
cucumber
Diet Dressing Nos 1 or 2

Clean all the vegetables quickly under running water and shake them dry. Break up the head of cauliflower into small sprigs, cut the carrots into sticks, but leave them whole if they are very small, trim the radishes leaving the best leaves on them (these are a good source of vitamins and minerals), wipe the peppers with a damp cloth and cut them in halves down the length in order to flush out the seeds under running water, then remove the core and membranes inside, trim the onions leaving the tender green leaves on them and cut the celery, when cleaned, into quarters through the heart also retaining the tender green leaves. Simply top and tail the courgettes and slice the cucumber into 2-inch chunks.

Arrange all the vegetables in attractive groups on a large meat-dish, placing the peppers cut side down. The dressing can either be served in a bowl placed in the centre of the dish before the vegetables are grouped around it, or served in a small bowl for each person. In any case, make plenty of it. Multiply the quantity given on page 67 by the number of people to be served, and add one extra quantity 'for the pot'. When prepared, put the dish into the refrigerator for half an hour before serving, to dry the vegetables thoroughly and make them crisp. This is one dish where the calorie count is so low, you will stop eating long before you reach 100c.

The Italian family way of serving spinach as a first course is excellent, and very appetising.

ITALIAN SPINACH SALAD (Spinacci al Agro) (serves 4)

2 lb washed and picked spinach
1 tablespoon lemon juice
½ teaspoon salt (optional)

freshly ground black pepper to taste
3 tablespoons good olive oil

Put the prepared spinach into a large saucepan with no more water than that which clings to the leaves after washing. Put a tight lid on the pan and cook over a moderate heat until the spinach is just tender and retains a crisp quality. Press out all the moisture until the spinach is quite dry.

While it is cooking beat the salt very well into the lemon juice, add pepper to taste and finally beat in the oil until the mixture is cloudy. Pour on to the spinach while it is still hot, turn over and over until it is well impregnated, and chill well before serving. Calorie count, 105c per portion.

Cottage cheese of the type already described is a very useful ingredient when planning diet menus. It is filling, and can be made into some very appetising dishes to be eaten either as a first course at dinner or as a main course at lunch.

SPRING APPETISER (serves 4)

4 tablespoons cottage cheese
8 tablespoons skimmed
milk
4 skinned tomatoes
8 spring onions
half a large green or sweet
red pepper

half a small cucumber
freshly milled black
pepper
salt (optional)
1 teaspoon lemon juice
1 tablespoon chopped
parsley

In a large bowl beat the cottage cheese and the skimmed milk until it resembles a thick but mobile cream, and add plenty of pepper and a little lemon juice if necessary, instead of salt. Then beat in the chopped parsley. Do not peel the cucumber but chop it into small cubes by slicing down the cucumber five times one way and five times the other, then cutting it across in thick slices. Roughly chop the tomatoes into similar-sized pieces, and slice the seeded pepper into cubes also. Trim the spring onions and cut them into small thick slices, green part as well, and mix all these ingredients into the cottage cheese. Sprinkle with a little more black pepper or parsley and chill for half an hour before serving in small bowls. Calorie count, 64c per portion.

When this same quantity is divided into six first course servings, the calorie count for each person is 43c.

Another very low calorie first course especially welcome in the hot weather is: .

COLD CUCUMBER APPETISER (serves 4)

2 tablespoons cottage cheese
6 tablespoons skimmed milk
2 cartons fat-free
yoghurt
juice of 1 lemon

1 medium sized cucumber
black Jamaican pepper
chopped parsley for
garnishing

Beat the cottage cheese, milk and yoghurt to a thick cream in a large bowl and grate the washed but unpeeled cucumber into it. Season well with ground black pepper and a little lemon juice. Cover the bowl and leave to chill for one hour. During this time the cucumber will make a certain amount of liquid but if the mixture is still very thick thin it down with a little more lemon juice or skimmed milk. Wheatgerm sprinkled on top is delicious. Calorie count, 71c per portion (exclusive of wheatgerm).

The Oatmeal and Apple Porridge recommended on the Health Diet can be made in a few moments the night before it is required. The coarse oatmeal used can be obtained at all health food shops.

OATMEAL AND APPLE PORRIDGE (serves 1)

1 tablespoon coarse oatmeal
2–3 tablespoons skimmed milk

half a medium sized crisp eating apple

Put the oatmeal into a small cereal dish and cover with skimmed milk. Put a plate over it and leave until the following morning. When required, grate the unpeeled apple into the oatmeal, mix well and serve. The calorie count is 144c per portion. The daily ration of wheatgerm can be sprinkled on top. When the diet permits, a teaspoonful of honey and/or a few raisins can be added after the grated apple.

METHOD FOR SKIMMING WHOLE MILK

In an emergency if commercially skimmed milk is not available, buy the silver-topped, cheapest variety and stand it in the refrigerator for an hour or so until the cream rises to the top. Pour off the first two inches from the bottle (to be used by non-dieting members of the family), and pour the rest into a shallow wide-topped bowl, the mixing bowl will do quite well. Leave without disturbing the surface until the milk fats rise again, then skim with a large metal spoon by drawing it gently over the surface. Now pass about half a dozen bands of clean tissue or greaseproof paper across the surface of the milk which will remove the remainder of the cream. The effectiveness of this method can be clearly seen when de-greasing hot soup in the same way. After passing the bands of tissue paper over it, not a single bead of fat will remain on the surface.

Many people like to make their own yoghurt, not only for economy's sake in a large family, but also in order to obtain their preferred consistency. The following very simple method produces five servings which are the equivalent of five individual cartons and cost much less.

HOME-MADE YOGHURT

1 pint (0.562 litre or 20 fl. oz) *skimmed milk*	*half an individual (5 oz) carton or 2½ tablespoons of commercially made unflavoured yoghurt*

On the first day place the yoghurt in a plastic bowl (with a snap-on lid) and beat smooth with a fork. Meanwhile heat the milk until warm to the touch of the little finger, then beat it into the contents of the bowl, stirring thoroughly. Snap the lid on to the bowl and wrap it all up in a thick bath-towel or a small blanket. Place in a warm airing cupboard for 8 hours (no more) until the yoghurt is coagulated. Then it can be chilled before serving.

On the second day replace the half carton of commercially made yoghurt with 2 large tablespoons of the home-made yoghurt. Heat the milk and proceed as on the previous day.

This process can be repeated five or six times before starting again with the commercial variety.

Using skimmed milk or fat-free milk and the plain unflavoured yoghurt sold in all supermarkets does ensure perfect results.

THE PREPARATION OF GREEN SALAD

Cut off a slice from the root end of the lettuce, or other salad, and place it in a large deep bowl in which there is

1 inch of water, no more. The object is for the leaves to drink through the root. Let it remain for *at least 1 hour* in a cool, dark place, when the outside wilted leaves will be found crisp and the whole plant refreshed. Then remove any bruised outside leaves and hold the lettuce under running cold water so that grit or insects are washed away. Now pick off the leaves and wash away any soil still adhering; shake free of as much water as possible using either a wire salad basket or a clean tea-towel loosely held by the corners and swung at arm's length. Pack the salad, without pressing it down, in a large plastic bowl with a tightly fitting lid and place it in the refrigerator for the contents to crisp and dry until required.

Prepared in this way very little of the salad is wasted (as usually happens when it is wilted), and it will keep fresh and crisp in the plastic bowl for several days. Never leave a salad with its leaves soaking in water.

Always use a large bowl to serve the salad in. This enables the leaves to be lightly turned over and over without bruising them.

Chapter 6

Cooked Vegetable Dishes, Field Fare and Rare Treats

The old French country method of cooking vegetables without water retains all their flavour and the maximum percentage of their natural properties. This method does make essential the acquisition of a very heavy gauge metal pan with a well-fitting lid, known in France as a *cocotte*. In a thin pan the contents will scorch. In order to make a pan lid fit very tightly a sheet of greaseproof paper laid over the rim of the pan before the lid is fixed down on to it will do the trick.

A dish of mixed vegetables cooked in this way is delicious. All root vegetables can be used, even the humble swede so much more attractively known as *rutabagas* to the Americans and French. When masked with Diet Dressing Nos 1 or 2, it makes a very good main course or a dish to serve at a dinner party to accompany steak or roast meat of any kind, especially when the latter must be served without gravy for those who are dieting.

LÉGUMES A L'ÉTUVÉE (Vegetable Casserole) (serves 4)

1 large onion	*coarse salt (or lemon juice)*
4 small leeks	*black pepper*
4 medium sized carrots	*chopped parsley*
half a small white cabbage	*1 teaspoon butter (or good*
1 medium sized swede	*olive oil)*
(rutabagas)	

Clean the vegetables quickly chop the onion and cut off the under running water, do not let tough green leaves of the leek them soak in it. Skin and roughly reserving the tender green part and cut into slices. Thinly peel and slice the carrots and the swede and cut them into pieces about the thickness of a 10p piece. Cut the cabbage into $\frac{1}{4}$ inch thick slices. Rub the butter thickly over the inside of the *cocotte* or smear the oil over it evenly. Put a layer of coarsely chopped onion in the bottom (this is what creates the necessary moisture) and a layer of sliced leeks on top. Sprinkle with a few grains of sea salt, or drops of lemon juice if preferred, and a little pepper. Next add a layer of carrots and season them, and spread the slices of cabbage over this. Season as before and if there are any leeks left, add these now before covering the whole with a layer of any remaining vegetables and finishing off with a layer of over-lapping slices of swede. Season this last layer, fix the lid firmly on the *cocotte* and put it on top of the cooker over a moderate temperature for 3 minutes. This will start the layer of onions simmering in the bottom of the pan. The heat should then be reduced to a low temperature and the pan left undisturbed for 20 minutes. By this time sufficient steam will have been created to cook the vegetables in their own juices and the lid can be removed for testing. Pierce the swede with a skewer and if not sufficiently tender replace the lid quickly and cook for a further 5 to 10 minutes. Tilt the *cocotte* carefully to see if there is any excess liquid in the bottom, in which case remove the lid and increase the heat to evaporate the liquid. This dish should be served direct from the *cocotte*, which can be draped in a folded white cloth for better presentation. Calorie count, 55c per portion.

This *étuvée* or smothered method is the most delicious way of cooking any vegetables but the mixture given is one of the best.

Another version of this dish which cooks more quickly and is more presentable at a dinner party is a

CHARLOTTE DE LÉGUMES (Vegetable Charlotte) (serves 6)

1 medium sized onion	*$\frac{1}{2}$ lb small green peas*
$\frac{1}{2}$ lb (226.8 g) young carrots	*(frozen can be used in an emergency)*
$\frac{1}{2}$ lb fine French beans	*$\frac{1}{2}$ lb swedes (rutabagas)*
$\frac{1}{2}$ lb very young turnips	*Diet Dressing Nos 1 or 2 (quantity for 4, page 67)*

Choose from your kitchen equipment a measuring bowl and a thick-bottomed pan or *cocotte* with a tight lid. The pan must hold five times the content of the bowl when filled. Wash, scrape and peel or top and tail the vegetables and put them, in the given order, into the *cocotte* which must have neither fat nor water in it ... a layer of chopped onion, a bowlful of grated carrots, a bowlful of French beans broken into 1 inch pieces, a bowlful of grated turnips, a bowlful of green peas and a bowlful of swedes cut into very small cubes. Spread each layer evenly over the surface of the pan, but do not press them down, and do not add any seasoning whatsoever. Put a tight lid on the pan and set it over a fairly high temperature for 3 to 5 minutes to start the cooking, then reduce the heat to simmering point and continue cooking for a further 20 minutes, until the swedes are cooked when tested with the point of a knife. Take off the lid and increase the heat to evaporate the juices that the vegetables will have made. Unmould the charlotte carefully on to a well-heated serving dish and pour the dressing over it. Serve at once. Seasoning may be added individually if it is found necessary, and the dressing may be served very gently heated if preferred to cold. Calorie count 42c per portion exclusive of dressing.

Any green beans are delicious cooked by this same method using the chopped onion and/or hearts of lettuce to provide the necessary moisture. Kidney or stick beans, often tasteless when cooked in water, can be very good when trimmed and cut slantwise into $\frac{1}{2}$ inch wide pieces and cooked with onion, pepper and parsley in this way.

Summer vegetables are at their best when cooked as follows, but they must be young ones, especially the peas.

SUMMER VEGETABLES (serves 4)

1 firm heart lettuce   *1 teaspoon butter (optional)*
$\frac{1}{2}$ lb young carrots   *1 medium sized onion*
1 lb young green peas

Wash the lettuce quickly under running water and trim off the root. Cut into quarters and place in the bottom of a thick heavy pan, which has first been well buttered with half the given quantity of butter. Peel and chop the onion into small pieces and put these on top of the lettuce, cover with the scraped and sliced carrots and the shelled peas. Put the rest of the butter on top, divided into tiny pieces, cover with a greaseproof paper, and seal with a tightly fitting lid. Place over a low heat and leave undis- turbed for 15 minutes when the contents should be cooked to a tender yet crisp quality. Season lightly with salt and pepper and turn into a hot dish. Serve with the liquor the vegetables have made. Calorie count, 57c per portion with butter—43c without.

If the diet does not allow butter, season the cooked veget- ables and mix in 1 teaspoon of freshly chopped mint.

When salt is used it should not be added to green vegetables until they are ready to be served. Added before this, it will draw both flavour and minerals out of them.

Any liquid made during cooking by this method, if not served, should be reserved and added to broth or stock.

Brussels Sprouts are with us for such a long period of the year, it is a good idea to present them sometimes in a new guise. To retain their mineral properties and also for digestion's sake, it is preferable to steam instead of boiling them.

BRUSSELS SPROUTS (serves 4)

1 lb (approx. 500 g) small Brussels sprouts
1 dessertspoon grated Spanish onion
1 medium sized Cox's

apple (or any hard, crisp eating apple)
black pepper and coarse salt
1 tablespoon chopped parsley

Remove the outside leaves of the sprouts, a sliver from the root end and cut a deep cross into it with a sharp-pointed knife. Put them into a metal colander and wash quickly in cold water. Shake free of moisture and place the colander over a pan half full of boiling water. Cover with a greaseproof paper and the pan lid and steam for 20 minutes. This should be enough to make the sprouts tender but not too soft. Chop them up finely, add the grated onion, the grated, unpeeled apple, and black pepper and a little salt to taste. Mix well, serve in a very hot vegetable dish and garnished with chopped parsley. Calorie count, 34c per portion.

The small amount of butter allowed on some diets can be made into an excellent sauce to serve with a dish of vegetables (or with fish). It is the method of combining the two simple ingredients which produces the unexpected result.

LEMON SAUCE (serves 4)

6 teaspoons butter
(preferably unsalted)
1 tablespoon lemon juice

A pinch of salt
black pepper

Put the lemon juice and a pinch of salt into a small thick pan to heat at a moderate temperature. Do not allow it to boil. Reduce the heat under the pan to minimum and, beating continually with a wooden fork, add the butter in tiny pieces until the mixture is creamy. As soon as all the butter is incorporated, add pepper and serve at once. Made in this way there is no danger of the butter running to oil as it can when heated first and the lemon juice added afterwards. This method also produces a thicker consistency. Calorie count, 80c per portion.

Some vegetables are best baked in the oven in their natural state. Courgettes (zucchini or summer squash) should be wiped with a damp cloth, topped and tailed and placed unpeeled and whole in an earthenware casserole, sprinkled with salt, a little lemon juice and black pepper and covered over tightly with tinfoil. Baked in a moderate oven, when prepared in this way they will create sufficient moisture to cook in their own juice and be full of flavour.

Aubergines or egg plant are equally delicious when washed, dried and baked whole just as they are, like jacket potatoes. When they are soft to the touch they can be split in two lengthways, served in their skins, and seasoned with soy sauce and pepper.

In order to braise the white Belgian endive as a winter vegetable it must first be blanched in hot water for five minutes, drained and squeezed as dry as possible and then baked in the oven dotted with the day's ration of butter, or sprinkled with salt, pepper and lemon juice.

Small round beetroot make a good vegetable dish after being washed in warm water (do not break the skin) and baked whole in the oven without being topped or tailed (this would make them bleed). When cooked for about 1 hour in a moderate oven they can be skinned, cut in two horizontally, sprinkled with a little tarragon vinegar, and covered with a portion of Diet Dressing No. 2.

Many complete and satisfying diet meals can be made with vegetables and a little cheese, and for this purpose a devilled cheese mixture gives the most flavour.

DEVILLED CHEESE MIXTURE (serves 2)

2 oz (56.7 g) Cheddar   *1 teaspoon tarragon vinegar*
or Cheshire cheese   *1 teaspoon soy sauce (or*
1 saltspoon dry mustard   *mushroom ketchup)*
1 teaspoon French mustard

Mix the dry mustard to a paste with the vinegar and when smooth add the soy sauce and the French mustard. Crumble the cheese or chop it up in small pieces and mix it well into the mustard mixture. Leave to marinate for half an hour if possible before using. Calorie count, 94c per portion.

This mixture can be used to fill pre-cooked mushrooms or artichoke hearts which are then placed under a hot grill until the devilled cheese bubbles and browns, or to cover pre-grilled tomato halves which are then browned in the same way. One large tomato served like this will constitute a much more satisfying meal in cold weather than if the same ingredients were served as a sliced tomato and a piece of cheese.

The mixed vegetable dish traditional in Southern France and known as *Ratatouille* is excellent for filling out diet menus. The Provençal recipe has one or two variations, but since we have adopted it in this country it is sometimes so full of variations as to be unrecognisable . . . the original cannot be improved upon. The two tablespoons of virgin olive oil essential for the classic flavour, when spread over a dish for eight people, do not count highly in calories. Count 73c for each serving and it is a meal in itself.

RATATOUILLE (serves 8)

1 lb (approx. 500 g) aubergines (egg plant)
1 lb Spanish onions
1 lb courgettes (zucchini)
2 lb (approx. 1 kilogramme) large tomatoes

1 clove garlic
2 tablespoons virgin olive oil (best quality)
coarse salt
black pepper

It is worthwhile for the authenticity of the dish to look for the thick-fleshed, flavoursome tomatoes imported from Mediterranean countries, and grown in America under the name of Beefsteak tomatoes. Wash them quickly under running water and cut into quarters. Skin the onions and chop them roughly, wash the aubergines and the courgettes and cut both into thick chunks, but do not peel them. In a heavy metal *cocotte* with a tight lid put the olive oil and the crushed clove of garlic, on top of the cooker on a low heat. When the oil is hot, pile in all the prepared vegetables, add a little coarse salt and some freshly milled pepper, put on the lid and cook until the mixture starts to bubble. Now turn down the heat to slow simmering point and cook for at least 2 hours, stirring now and again. Leave the lid on the *cocotte* during this time and the Ratatouille will be found to have made a considerable quantity of liquid. To reduce this, remove the lid, increase the heat and cook a little more rapidly for 10 to 15 minutes. This dish must cook very slowly. When ready to serve it should be of a thick soupy consistency and can be eaten either hot or cold.

Tradition does allow a couple of chopped peppers, green and sweet red, to be added to the ingredients to be cooked, and a sprinkling of chopped parsley for decoration when served.

An egg and onion dish, the diet relation of Oeufs Soubise, is none the less appetising for the flour and butter-bound sauce of the original being replaced by a hot yoghurt sauce flavoured with mustard.

EGGS SOUBISE (serves 4)

4 medium sized onions
4 eggs
1 saltspoon coarse salt
crystals

white and black pepper
6 tablespoons plain yoghurt
1 teaspoon French mustard
1 saltspoon mustard seed

Peel and roughly chop the onions and place in a small thick pan with 2 tablespoons of cold water. Fit on a tight lid and cook over a gentle heat for 10 minutes. Then remove the lid, increase the heat and cook until the onions are tender and their liquor re-absorbed. Remove the pan from direct heat and then add 2 tablespoons of yoghurt. Season with a little coarse salt, plenty of white pepper and keep warm. Meanwhile soft-boil the eggs, crack the shell all over with the bowl of a teaspoon and remove it with the inverted end. During this time gently heat the rest of the yoghurt (but not to boiling point), flavour it with the French mustard added a little at a time, season with black pepper and keep warm. To serve, divide the cooked onion between four heated serving dishes, place a peeled egg in the centre of each and mask with the hot, flavoured yoghurt. Decorate with a few grains of mustard seed. Calorie count, 112c per portion.

If preferred, French mustard can be replaced with a fine sliver of garlic crushed and added to the yoghurt while it is heating; the dish is then decorated with paprika.

A savoury vegetable aspic makes a satisfying lunch for dieters in the summer, and has the decorative appearance necessary to tempt heavy meat-eaters who must cut down on protein.

VEGETABLE MOULD (serves 4)

4 breakfastcups skinned
chopped tomatoes
$\frac{1}{3}$ cup chopped onion
$\frac{1}{4}$ cup chopped celery leaves
1 cup finely chopped celery
1 teaspoon coarse salt
1 teaspoon brown sugar
black pepper to taste
3 bayleaves

3 cloves
2 tablespoons powdered
gelatine
$\frac{1}{2}$ cup tomato juice
$\frac{1}{4}$ cup cold water
3 tablespoons lemon juice
Tabasco sauce
Escoffier sauce

Combine and gently heat the tomato juice, onion, celery leaves, salt, pepper, bayleaves, sugar and cloves. Soften the gelatine in the cold water, dissolve this in the heated tomato juice, add a few drops of Tabasco sauce, a teaspoon of Escoffier sauce, and the chopped celery. Remove the bayleaves and the cloves and check the seasoning. Pour into a wetted mould and chill until set. Unmould and serve on a bed of watercress. Calorie count, 61c per portion.

FIELD FARE

In early spring the countryside offers many wild vegetables that were once in common usage and eagerly awaited by country people, not only as a free-to-all change from winter root vegetables but as a spring tonic of medicinal value.

Some of these plants were made into potions, wines and cordials, but many of them were cooked as vegetables or eaten raw, and still are.

In parts of Norfolk and Suffolk the sale of rock samphire, or 'sanfer' as the countryfolk call it, is general in shops, markets and wayside stalls. This wild vegetable so popular in the nineteenth century seems now to have been forgotten in other parts of England. It grows in many countries not necessarily on the sea shore as its Latin name *Chrithmum maritimum* would indicate, but in stony, sandy ground generally. Both leaves and thick stems are cooked and eaten like asparagus, or used raw in salads or pickled in vinegar and spices to eat with cold meats.

Wild sea kale can be cooked and eaten in the same way and many country people relish the young shoots of wild ferns, cut when they are still curled tightly and only four or five inches above the ground. Champions of this delicacy swear that it rivals asparagus.

Young nettle tops cooked as a vegetable must not be dismissed before trial. They have a high content of valuable minerals, in texture and flavour they rival spinach and, extremely important, they are the only vegetable which escapes chemical fertilisers. Nettles picked when not more than 2 inches tall and cooked in the correct fashion have a velvety texture much more appetising than the rather slithery consistency of spinach. As a spring nature cure for the complexion they are unrivalled.

A famous old country recipe for 'clearing the blood and improving the complexion in Spring' was to take a daily wineglassful of nettle beer.

More practical, and very delicious, is to serve young nettle tops as a vegetable three or four times a week (according to one recipe or another) during the period of their edible state, which lasts from three weeks to a month in the early spring. This coincides conveniently with that difficult period when one is tired of winter vegetables and the young spring vegetables are either not yet available or prohibitive in price. Even in this world of diminishing fields and open country, nettles flourish wherever grass grows.

TO COOK YOUNG NETTLE TOPS

Armed with a pair of gardening gloves, some scissors and a 4-pint capacity pan, snip off the young nettle tops when they are no more than 2 inches high (a patch of nettles that has recently been scythed will produce a new crop perfect for this dish). When the pan is full and loosely piled high, it will produce a serving for two people.

Empty the panful into a large colander and hold it under running cold water for a few moments. This will be enough to clean the snippets, as they are not sandy and difficult to clean like spinach. Shake the contents free of excess water, pile the nettle tops into the pan, fix on the lid tightly and cook over medium heat for 10 minutes, shaking the pan occasionally. The moisture adhering to the greens and the sealed pan will create enough steam to cook them without water. Don't over-cook. Drain and press out any excess moisture with a large spoon, season now (greens should not be salted during the cooking), chop roughly and dot with half the day's butter ration if on the Balanced Diet.

Serve either to accompany steak or roast meat or as a luncheon dish. This can have many variations.

The cooked nettle-tops can be made into a complete meal by serving each portion in an individual ovenware dish topped with a well-drained poached egg; or served extra hot and masked with a portion of cold Diet Dressing No. 1;

or with grated Gruyère cheese sprinkled thickly on top of each portion to cover the surface completely and then browned to the bubbling stage under a pre-heated grill.

Call them *Orties Printinières*, extol the cosmetic value of this 'new vegetable', do not divulge its nature to the unadventurous until each dish is empty, and your stock as a *cordon bleu* will soar.

One of the best-known wild spring greens and an unrivalled source of iron and vitamins, is young dandelions. They are sold every season by the most exclusive Parisian greengrocers as a salad delicacy as soon as they appear. This, in the British Isles, is in February/March depending on the region. Only good when eaten raw, they become very bitter when cooked, as I have discovered.

The small rosettes of dog-toothed green leaves must be lifted whole from the ground when they are not more than 2 inches in diameter, and the smaller the better. Dig them up with a sharp-pointed knife keeping the plant whole, the leaves held together by the small nutty flavoured root which is delicious.

Scrape and trim this root without detaching it from the leaves and clean the tiny plants quickly, holding them in a colander under swiftly running water. Shake them dry at once and transfer to a salad basket or a clean tea-cloth, and swing at arm's length until free of excess moisture, then put them to crisp for an hour in a large plastic bowl closed with a tight lid, in the refrigerator. When required, dress with either French or L.P. Dressing.

To make a very good luncheon dish toss each portion in Diet Dressing No. 1 and scatter a tablespoon of grated cheese on top. The best of all is a Dandelion Salad dressed with walnut oil and tarragon vinegar, which is the king of salads.

RARE TREATS

Some sweet dishes are not excluded from diet menus. They are important in staving off the growing craving for something other than savoury dishes which creeps up on most dieters at some time or other. This can become especially acute in people who have been used to eating creamy desserts, and the recipes which follow also cater to this consistency gap.

ORANGE AND APPLE CREAM (serves 4)

4 cartons unflavoured
yoghurt (low fat)
1 medium sized orange

2 large Cox's apples
(Green Pippins or any hard
eating apple)

Wash the orange and the apples and dry them. Empty the yoghurt into a mixing bowl and grate the orange peel into it. Now squeeze the orange and add the juice, and finally grate into the mixture the unpeeled apples. Mix well and chill before serving. Calorie count, 81c per portion.

If you are on a diet at strawberry time and yearn for thick cream to eat with them, stop yearning and try *Fromage Blanc* to eat with your fruit instead. The average French family eats it in preference to cream with all soft fruits, and its cost, both from a budget and a calorie point of view, makes it interesting.

FROMAGE BLANC (serves 4)

4 tablespoons cottage cheese
8 tablespoons skimmed milk

Put the cottage cheese into a large serving bowl and beat in the skimmed milk, a little at a time until the required consistency is obtained. The mixture should be thick and smooth. The calorie count for each serving is 42c as against 262c for the same amount of cream.

A very delicious sweet course indeed, whether you judge by dietary standards or not, can be made when a small quantity of honey is allowed on the diet.

BACCHANTE'S CREAM (serves 4)

6 tablespoons cottage cheese	2 teaspoons clear liquid honey
4/6 tablespoons skimmed milk	1 tablespoon brandy
	4 saltspoons powdered coffee, freshly milled

Mix the skimmed milk into the cottage cheese with a fork until it is like thick cream, and add the honey, previously warmed if necessary to make it quite liquid. Then beat in the brandy and last of all the very finely powdered coffee. Incorporate all the ingredients well by beating firmly and divide the cream between four very small china soufflé dishes. Scatter a pinch of powdered coffee on top of each one and keep in a cool place until required. The calorie count for each person is 84c.

COFFEE CURD

For those on a very stringent diet the above recipe can be adapted, missing out the honey and brandy, simply mixing the cheese with sufficient skimmed milk to make the preparation smooth and then flavouring it with finely powdered coffee, a little more than indicated above to compensate for the other flavours eliminated. This, however, does bring the calorie count down to 57c per person.

It often happens when buying apricots and peaches in England, that they are found to be not sufficiently ripe to eat raw, having been left to mature in the box on the journey from their place of origin. They can also be rather tasteless, and the way to remedy this is to make them into a real compôte cooked in an earthenware casserole in the oven as opposed to being cooked in a metal saucepan and stewed on top of the cooker. The method makes all the difference to the flavour.

COMPÔTE OF FRUIT (serves 4)

1¼ lb (approx. 500 g) fresh apricots (peaches can be used instead)	2 dessertspoons honey
	1 lemon
	cold water

Halve the fruit by cutting it around the circumference with a sharp knife and twisting the two halves in opposite directions. Place the fruit cut side downwards in a large earthenware casserole. Prepare the syrup by melting the honey to liquid consistency and mixing in first the juice of the lemon and then $1\frac{1}{2}$ to 2 teacups of warm water. This should be just sufficient to come halfway up to the level of the fruit. Put the lid on the casserole and cook very gently in the bottom of the oven heated to a low temperature. Test with a long-pronged cooking fork and remove from the oven when not quite cooked. Leave the lid on the casserole so that the fruit will finish cooking without losing its shape. Calorie count, 45c per portion.

Apples and pears make a good winter compôte when cooked in this way with fresh orange juice instead of lemon, honey and water.

Bananas make a very good sweet dish when skinned and cut in half lengthways, sprinkled liberally with lemon juice and baked in a hot oven for 15 minutes or grilled (broiled) for 7 to 10 minutes until soft and browned on top.

Cold grapefruit presents a forbidding appearance to some dieters, but if the prepared halves are grilled (broiled) until hot and golden brown, even non-grapefruit eaters will accept them willingly. Alternatively, the fruit can be baked for about 20 minutes in a moderate oven.

Before cooking them the dieting hostess can christen each guest's half with a measure of sherry but not her own, unless she counts the cost.

A delicious low-calorie sorbet can be made with mandarines when in season.

MANDARINE SORBET (serves 2)
2 large mandarines   *1 teaspoon chopped mint*
4 large ice cubes

Peel the mandarines and remove all threads and pith by scraping the fruit with the blunt edge of a knife, separate the sections and put them into a liquidiser. Two or three minutes before serving put the ice cubes inside a folded tea-towel and crush into pieces with a hammer. Put them in the liquidiser with the fruit and blend until the ice is in crystals and the mixture of a thick consistency. Stir, pour into tall glasses and garnish with chopped mint when available. Serve immediately. This sorbet must be made at the last moment or it will liquefy completely. Calorie count, 18c per portion.

Chapter 7

Fish, Meat and Broths

Those who have savoured the refinements of Japanese food will know that fish does not have to be cooked to be very good indeed, and in fact when eaten in its natural state fish retains not only its full flavour but also the full value of its nutritional qualities. This method of preparation is best for small fish of the firm-fleshed varieties such as trout, and its first cousin the grayling which is also caught in American waters. Red and grey mullet, equally suitable for this purpose, are European in their habitat, but bass and perch are common both sides of the Atlantic. If caught small enough these can be quite delicious, not only as a diet fish, but as a first course for a dinner party far superior to the conventional pickled fish.

Have the fish gutted and the head cut off by the fish-monger. If he will skin and fillet it, so much the better; if not, it is quite easily done in the following way: Place the fish flat on the cutting board and with a small sharp-pointed knife cut off the dorsal fins and then make a slight incision through them from the head end to the tail. Cut off the fins on the belly and make another small incision down the length of the fish. Dip the finger tips in salt and work up a little flap of skin at the tail end with the thumb nail. Draw the skin backwards to the head. It will come off quite easily. Turn the fish over and skin the other side. Now cut through the dorsal slit towards the centre, pressing the knife on to the backbone; repeat from the belly slit towards the backbone removing the whole fillet. Turn the fish over and insert the point of the knife under the exposed back-bone in the centre and cut towards the tail end. Lift up the freed bone and work the knife blade up towards the head end, thus removing the second fillet from the bone. Cut each one in two lengthways to form 4 fillets in all.

PICKLED LEMON FISH (serves 4)

*1 small red/grey mullet,
grayling or trout (½ lb
(226.8 g) weight when
prepared)*

*1 large lemon
1 bayleaf and 6 black peppercorns
paprika*

Grate the lemon rind coarsely, squeeze the juice into a long shallow dish and mix in the rind, crumbled bayleaf, and the crushed peppercorns. Prick the fillets all over with a sharp-pronged cooking fork and lay them in the marinade, turning them over several times to coat them thoroughly. Leave in a cool place covered for 4 hours, turning them every half-hour. The fish when ready will have become quite firm and white as though cooked till just tender. To serve, remove the fish from the marinade at the very last minute.

Lay the fillets briefly on a piece of kitchen paper to remove excess moisture, cut each one slant-wise into five small strips about ½ inch wide and dust them liberally with paprika. Place each serving on a small decorative plate garnished with three black olives and some of the tender green leaves of celery. Calorie count, approx. 24c per portion (exclusive of olives). A very thin slice of wholewheat bread or crisp bread (on the Balanced Diet) completes this course.

Herrings can be scaled or skinned, filleted and cooked in the same marinade to provide a new form of soused herring much more delicate in flavour than those cooked with vinegar.

HERRINGS IN LEMON SAUCE (serves 4)

*1 lb (approx. 500 g) (prepared
weight) small herrings
1 lemon (2 tablespoons
juice)*

*2 bayleaves
6 black peppercorns
paprika
cold water*

Have the herrings gutted, scaled, and filleted and prepare the marinade as for the previous recipe. Sprinkle each fillet with paprika, crumbled bayleaf, crushed peppercorns and grated lemon peel, place them in half the lemon juice to

soak for an hour, and sprinkle the rest of the lemon juice over them. Now make each fillet into a tight roll and place them close together in a small oven-proof serving dish. To the marinade add an equal quantity of cold water and pour it over the herrings. Cover with a lid or a piece of foil and bake in a moderate oven for $\frac{3}{4}$ hour. Allow to cool and garnish with very thin slices of lemon sprinkled with chopped parsley before serving. Calorie count, approx. 218c per portion.

All small fish such as bream, mullet, grayling or fresh haddock are delicious when baked whole in the oven in the following way.

BAKED FISH WITH HERBS (serves 4)

1½ lb (680 g) fish when prepared
3 large tomatoes
1 onion

black pepper (salt optional)
1 teaspoon dried basil
1 large lemon

Place the fish in a fireproof serving dish and grate the lemon peel coarsely over it, then strain the lemon juice on top, basting the fish well and scattering a little freshly ground black pepper and half the basil over it. Peel and slice the onion into very thin rings and place a layer over the fish, sprinkle with pepper and cover with the tomatoes skinned, sliced and sprinkled with pepper and the rest of the basil. Cover with foil and bake in a moderately hot oven for 30 to 40 minutes according to the thickness of the fish. When a skewer pierces the whole thickness, the fish is cooked. Calorie count, approx. 109c per portion.

Grilled (broiled) fish of all varieties can be made appetising without any salt at all by using the ubiquitous lemon for flavouring, and as a condiment.

GRILLED FISH WITH LEMON

Prepare the fish and cut into serving portions, dot with half the day's butter ration or a teaspoon of good olive oil if on the Balanced Diet, and sprinkle liberally with lemon juice. Pre-heat the grill for 5 minutes before putting the fish under it. When the uppermost side starts to colour, turn the fish over carefully, baste with the juices and a little more lemon juice, sprinkle with freshly ground Jamaican pimento corns or black pepper and grill until golden brown and cooked. It is a good idea to grill the fish in a very flat fire-proof dish so that it can go to the table, with all its juices, in the dish in which it was cooked. The absence of salt is unnoticeable when plenty of lemon juice is used.

The butter or olive oil can be omitted on a fat-free diet and plain lemon juice used instead.

A very good Fish Pie can be made according to diet rules by replacing the flour, milk and butter sauce necessary to bind the ingredients with a preparation of yoghurt and eggs so well flavoured that even those averse to yoghurt do not recognise it and declare this dish more interesting than the original. It improves the flavour to include in the quantity of mixed fish given, a small amount of smoked haddock, say 3 ounces.

FISH PIE (serves 4)

1 lb (approx. 500 g) mixed fish (skate, cod, lemon sole, smoked haddock)
1 medium sized onion
1 lb swedes (rutabagas), or carrots and young turnips
2 cartons plain yoghurt (10 fl. oz)

2 large eggs
1 small sliver garlic (¼ clove) or garlic salt
black pepper and coarse salt
soy sauce
1 heaped tablespoon chopped parsley

Wash the white fish quickly under running water (cut off any fins or loose skin) and spread it over the bottom of a fireproof dish in one layer. Sprinkle with a little ordinary salt and black pepper, cover with foil and bake in a moderate oven for about 20 to 25 minutes depending on the thickness of the fish. When tender strain off all the liquor, remove all skin and bones and leave to cool. Cook the smoked haddock in a little water to draw off the excess salt, strain well when cooked and remove skin and bones. Be sure that there is no moisture left oozing from the fish and then break it into fairly large pieces with a fork.

Break the eggs into a bowl add a pinch of salt and plenty of black pepper beat lightly with a fork and add the yoghurt a little at a time and beating with a hand whisk, until the mixture is smooth and creamy. During this operation add half the chopped parsley and about ¼ teaspoonful of garlic salt or the small sliver of garlic crushed on a plate with the flat of a knife blade. Now add the cooked fish and mix well before turning the preparation into a deep soufflé dish which should be just large enough to hold the quantity with a half-inch to spare at the top of the dish. Cook in a bain-marie (a shallow tin half full of hot water) for about 40 minutes starting at 350 °F gas mark 3 for the first 10 minutes and then reducing the heat to 300 °F, gas mark 2/3. As your oven will probably have its own temperamental ways bear in mind that these heats can be varied accordingly, since the sauce must not cook too quickly or it will curdle.

Meanwhile cook the vegetables in the following way. Scrape the root vegetables and cut them into the thinnest possible slices so that they will cook in minimum time and peel and roughly chop the onion. Choose a thick heavy-gauge metal pan with a well-fitting lid and place the chopped onion over the bottom in one layer, sprinkle with a little salt and 1 tablespoon of cold water, and arrange the rest of the vegetables on top in layers, each one lightly seasoned with salt and black pepper. Cover the pan tightly with the lid and should it not fit well place a sheet of greaseproof paper over the rim of the pan before pressing down the lid to seal the pan completely.

Start cooking the contents over very low heat until a faint bubbling is heard (in about 3 minutes) then reduce the heat to the absolute minimum and continue to simmer for 15 to 20 minutes without removing the lid. The onion will make sufficient moisture to cook the vegetables in their own juice. When the vegetables are easily pierced with a knife, strain off any liquid which might remain (add it to a vegetable cocktail) and press the vegetables free of all moisture, mash to a smooth pulp, check the seasoning and return to the dry pan to keep hot.

When the fish preparation is set and just firm in the centre to finger pressure, lightly spread the *purée* on top, mark with the prongs of a fork and place under a very hot grill (or broiler), to brown slightly for about 3 minutes. Scatter the rest of the parsley on top and serve immediately. Calorie count, approx. 164c per portion.

A cold Fish Salad is a pleasant summer dish but for dieters it is usually ruled out because two of the main ingredients are rice and mayonnaise. Try this version. It is unusual both in contrasting flavours and consistencies.

FISH SALAD (serves 6)

1 lb (approx. 500 g) lobster or crab meat (or cooked white fish, turbot, hake or sole)	6 tablespoons Diet Dressing Nos 1 or 2
half a medium sized cauliflower	1 tablespoon chopped fennel leaves (or fresh tarragon or parsley)
1 tablespoon lemon juice	French mustard (optional)
black pepper and coarse salt	lettuce leaves or watercress

Cut the washed and dried cauliflower into slices $\frac{1}{8}$ inch thick and cut these across both ways to form tiny cubes, place in a large decorative serving bowl and sprinkle with the lemon juice, some freshly milled black pepper and a little coarse salt. Beat the fresh chopped herbs and 1 dessertspoon of French mustard (if used) into the Diet Dressing and mix this in with the prepared cauliflower. Place it in the refrigerator. Break the fish into convenient pieces with a fork and season to taste with coarse salt and some black pepper. Add this to the dressed cauliflower and turn over very gently with two forks in order to coat the ingredients with the dressing without breaking them any smaller. Garnish with lettuce leaves or watercress and serve slightly chilled, not iced. Calorie counts: Crab salad or Lobster Salad with Dressing No. 1, 165c per portion; White Fish Salad with Dressing No. 1, 119c per portion. Using the same recipe with Dressing No. 2 reduces the calorie count by 11c per portion.

The problem of meat dishes is an important one to solve especially when an all-protein diet is in question. An exclusive diet of fillet and sirloin steaks can strain any household budget.

There are, however, several very lean, cheaper cuts which can be substituted, and which are readily available if you take the trouble to enlist the help of your butcher.

One of the best is the small thick feather steak. This is also known as blade-bone steak which technically is part of the chuck, and chuck itself when prepared by the method for cooking these cheaper cuts can also be tender and full of flavour. The mysteriously named 'bolo' steak is also good and is cut from the top rump into small pieces of about 4 ounces, very convenient for dieters. All these can be found in supermarkets but I repeat, it is very worthwhile letting your butcher know that you are interested in these cuts so that he will save them for you.

Another cut of beef rarely used for grilling, or broiling to use the good old English word that they have had the good sense to retain in America, is flank steak. In England it is also called skirt, but that name overseas denotes a much less lean cut. In any case the one to ask for is fillet skirt or sirloin flank whichever side of the ocean you live on. This is the cut nearest to the sirloin or fillet (for *filet mignon*) and is therefore succulent. When it is a very thick piece (which can be as much as 3 inches) ask your butcher to split it through the centre; 1 inch thick is best.

Prepare the meat well in advance, during the morning if you are to serve it for dinner in the evening, and before breakfast if you are grilling it for lunch.

Lay the steak flat on the board, split side uppermost, pierce it all over with the prongs of a big cooking fork, and then sprinkle liberally with Meat Tenderiser. This excellent product, whose chief ingredient is dried ground papaya fruit, is obtainable from delicatessen stores and the big supermarkets throughout the country. It makes any meat deliciously tender. Having prepared the cut side of the meat now place it on the rack of the grill pan cut side down, and pierce the other side, again sprinkling it with Meat Tenderiser. Leave covered over in a cool place (but not in the refrigerator) until required.

To cook, pre-heat the grill (broiler) at maximum temperature for 5 minutes, place the prepared meat under it and grill for 4 minutes. Turn the meat, seal for 3 minutes, lower the heat to moderate and continue cooking for a further 3 to 5 minutes according to thickness. Ten minutes in all should be sufficient to cook a 1-inch thick steak, which should be served pink inside. Place it on a well-heated serving dish and slice with a sharp knife *across the grain*, into $\frac{1}{4}$-inch thick slices. Pour the juices from the grill pan over it and serve at once.

It will not need further seasoning when prepared with Meat Tenderiser, which can also be used to prepare feather and bolo cuts in the same way. These, however, will require no more than 4 minutes grilling on each side at maximum temperature to cook their ¾-inch thickness to perfection.

Fillet skirt or flank can also be used to prepare a very good diet dish which retains all of its natural properties, since the ingredients are not cooked at all.

STEAK TARTARE (serves 1 person)

*4 oz (approx. 120 g) raw
fillet skirt steak (sirloin
flank or tip) for each person
1 teaspoon chopped capers
1 teaspoon finely chopped
onion*

*1 teaspoon olive oil or 1 egg
yolk (not both)
1 pinch mustard
1 big pinch freshly milled
black pepper
1 teaspoon soy sauce
chopped parlsey to garnish*

Remove any skin or fat from the meat and pass it through the finest rings of the mincer directly on to the serving plate in order not to lose any of the juices. Form it into a round flat cake and make a few little holes with a skewer through the thickness. Mix the mustard and pepper into the soy sauce and add the oil if it is used. Beat this dressing well and pour it carefully over the meat-cake, filling the holes. Then decorate with the egg yolk placed in the centre (but not if oil is used instead). Arrange the chopped capers, grated onion and chopped parsley in circles around it. Each person will mix these ingredients together on their plate adding a little more soy sauce or pepper if necessary. Calorie count, using egg yolk, is approx. 224c and olive oil 238c per portion.

Alternatively, this dish is excellent made with a half portion of Dressing No. 1 and capers and onion, cutting out the egg and oil. Then the calorie count is reduced to 210c per portion.

The traditional accompaniment to Steak Tartare is hot toast, but those on the Balanced Diet need not deprive themselves if they eat with it half of their daily bread ration, cut into paper thin slices and browned under a hot grill. This will produce a Melba Toast much less trouble to make than the classic variety which is first toasted and then split in two. Make sure that really stale bread is used in order to obtain very thin slices.

For dieters who are allowed no bread whatsoever, provide either plain lettuce leaves or sticks of raw carrot and celery instead.

Black Pudding is the Frenchman's equivalent of sausage and mash, and costs even less both in calories and cash.

BLACK PUDDING AND APPLE RINGS (serves 4)

*12 oz (340.2 g) black
pudding*

*2 medium sized apples
(eaters or cookers as
preferred)*

Wipe the apples with a damp cloth, core but do not peel them, and slice each one into 4 thick rings. Place them on a very lightly buttered plate to prevent sticking and grill on both sides until soft and browned. Keep them hot. Slice the pudding across in slanting slices about ½ inch thick and grill for one minute on each side, just enough to make them thoroughly hot. Allow 3 slices for each person. Serve on a hot dish alternating the slices of black pudding and apple. Either French or English mustard can be served with this dish. Calorie count, approx. 246c per portion.

Liver in general should be cooked as described on page 61, and served sprinkled with lemon juice, black pepper and chopped parsley, but a pâté of chicken livers can be made quite simply and this makes a very good dieter's luncheon.

CHICKEN LIVER PÂTÉ (serves 1 for main course or 2 for a first course)

*2 whole chicken livers
1 teaspoon butter (from daily
ration)
1 teaspoon finely chopped
onion*

*1 big pinch marjoram
black pepper
lemon juice for seasoning*

Heat a small thick iron frying pan over a moderate heat for 3 to 4 minutes with nothing in it at all. Then put the butter into it and as soon as this melts put in the chicken livers wiped and trimmed of all threads and stained parts, and add the marjoram and black pepper. When one side is sealed and turns colour, turn the livers over, add the very finely chopped onion and the lemon juice (about $1\frac{1}{2}$ to 2 teaspoons), cook for a further 3 minutes and turn the whole panful, juices and all, into a small bowl. They should be just set but quite pink inside. Chop up the livers very finely with a sharp knife, mix well, check the seasoning, mix again, and smooth the pâté down in the bowl, marking the top with the tines of a fork. Leave to cool before serving. Calorie count, 118c if served as one portion.

If a very smooth pâté is preferred, turn the whole panful, once cooked, into an electric blender, carefully scraping out all the juices from the pan, and blend to the required consistency.

The following recipe for chicken, while originally created to conform to diet principles, also fills the need we all feel to have this bird flavoured in some different way, so often do we find ourselves eating it.

POUSSIN WITH LEMON AND GARLIC (serves 2)

1 small poussin	*1 large lemon or 2 small ones*
1 small onion	*1 dessertspoon soy sauce*
	$\frac{1}{4}$ teaspoon ground black
Marinade	*pepper*
1 tablespoon olive oil of good quality	*a small clove of garlic*

Cut the bird in half lengthways through the breastbone and remove the skin and wing-tips. Put them with the trimmed and washed giblets into a pan with the chopped onion and a half-pint of cold water. Cover and simmer for 35 minutes, removing the liver after the first 10 minutes, and reserving it for the sauce. Peel the lemons thickly without including the white pith and cut the peel into very narrow strips, and then across again into tiny cubes. This gives better results than grating it. Beat the soy sauce and black pepper into the olive oil and add half the juice of the lemon squeezed but not strained. Peel and crush the garlic with the blade of a knife and add to the marinade. Place the two halves of poussin outer-side downwards in it and leave covered in a cool place for at least 2 hours, basting once or twice. Pre-heat the grill for 3 minutes, then grill the bird still outer-side down in its marinade for 10 minutes. Turn the pieces over, baste well with the rest of the lemon juice and then the pan juices, and grill for a further 10 minutes, having reduced the heat slightly. When cooked remove to a heated serving dish and keep hot. To serve, crush the cooked liver with a fork and mix it in with the juices and the marinade in the cooking dish, before pouring it over the chicken. Decorate with watercress. Calorie count, 255c per portion.

This dish is also delicious when eaten cold. In this case the chicken is left to cool in its marinade after cooking and then drained on kitchen paper until quite cold and served with a green salad.

To cook the usual $3\frac{1}{2}$ lb chicken in this way, double the quantity of marinade and lemon juice and cut the chicken into eight pieces before skinning them. Marinade and cook as previously indicated.

The chicken stock made from the skin, trimmings and giblets will make a diet consommé to drink as an alternative to cold water, in the winter.

CHICKEN CONSOMMÉ
When the giblets and skin have simmered for 40 minutes to an hour, remove the pan from the heat and skim the liquid free of all fat by straining it first into a bowl and then drawing several bands of greaseproof paper across the surface until every bead of fat is removed. Season with a few drops of soy sauce and a little lemon juice.

The half pint quantity made with the poussin trimmings will serve two people. If a $3\frac{1}{2}$ lb bird is cooked the water added to the giblets can be increased to 1 pint and will serve four.

Calorie count, 56c per breakfastcup.

Another alternative to all the water that must be drunk in order to lose weight is the following broth:

BEAUTY BROTH (serves 3)

1 bunch watercress   *1 large carrot*
1 handful parsley   *cold water*
1 large onion

Skin and chop the onion, scrape the carrot and slice it into thin rings, wash and roughly chop the watercress and parsley, stalks and all, and put these vegetables into a large pan. Cover with 3 breakfastcups of cold water, put the lid on the pan and place it over a moderate heat. As soon as boiling point is reached remove the lid and continue simmering for 20 minutes, stirring once or twice. Strain the liquid into soup cups and season to taste with lemon juice. Calorie count, 17c per portion.

Any outside leaves left after trimming green vegetables, such as cabbage leaves, radish tops and the dark green leaves of leeks, can be chopped up and added to the above ingredients allowing 3 large breakfastcups of cold water to 2 heaped cups of chopped vegetables.

For those who long for a thick soup once in a while during a diet period the following Thick Celery Soup can be served as a mid-morning meal and will not break any diet rules even though it is very satisfying.

THICK CELERY SOUP (serves 4)

1 large head of celery   *cold water: 2¼ Imperial*
1 large onion   *pints (1.3 litres or 45 fl. oz)*
salt and black pepper   *chopped parsley*

Choose a head of celery with plenty of green leaves which are in good condition. These are essential to the flavour of the soup. Separate the sticks and scrub them all quickly under running cold water. Do not let them soak in it. Trim off stained parts and any damaged leaves and chop up the whole head into very small pieces, outside green sticks and green leaves as well. Skin and chop the onion and put it into a large pan. Place the celery on top and add sufficient cold water to cover, about $2\frac{1}{4}$ pints. Put a lid on the pan and set it over a medium heat to reach simmering point. Now skim off any froth that may have risen, lower the heat and cook at simmering point until the celery is tender. Pass the soup through a vegetable mill or an electric liquidiser, return it to the pan and season to taste. Reheat, stir very well to distribute the purée evenly and serve in small bowls in which a little chopped parsley has been sprinkled. When parsley is scarce, reserve a little of the green leaves of the celery finely chopped to scatter on the surface of the soup as it is served. Calorie count, 12c per portion.

Chapter 8

Exercises

The word exercise sounds menacing to the dieter's ears, but take heart, nature has a wonderful way of supplying the balance, and the increased energy which results from good dieting brings with it the urge to be active.

To be effective and enjoyed exercises must be performed smartly, briskly, consciously using all the muscles that are brought into play. In this way the movements will fulfil their purpose of expending the energy necessary to consume the calories supplied by the food eaten, at the same time working the muscles back to their original flexibility and power. This will not be accomplished by going through the exercises in a slack half-hearted manner just to quieten one's conscience with the fact that they have been performed. Other factors to note are:

Walk at a brisk pace, don't saunter along.
Music helps exercises to go at a swinging pace and in consequence they become a pleasure instead of a penance. Exercising with a willing companion also makes them easier, and in a group they can be fun.

The exercises most needed by all dieters are those which recondition the sagging abdomen muscles and help regain the flat front of youth. When achieved, this does wonders for the morale, as well.

To start with, always 'walk tall' stretching up to full height with the seat tucked in, head held straight on the neck with the chin tucked in, not poking forward, and the abdomen held *up* and in. This control, if carried out for a few minutes at a time to start with, will quickly become a habit.

The muscle exercises are as follows:
1. Get down on the floor on hands and knees with the head

hanging down between the shoulders. Draw in the abdomen muscles to touch the backbone, humping up your back at the same time. Relax, and repeat 10 times, raising the head as high as possible each time before lowering it between the shoulders.

Tuck head down as spine is raised

Raise head as spine is lowered

(1)

(2)

2. Lie on the floor leaning back on the forearms and with legs held together lift them as high as possible from the floor, keeping the knees stiff. Lower them slowly to the floor, relax, and repeat 10 times.

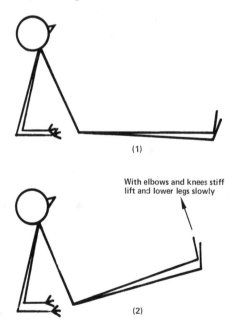

(1)

With elbows and knees stiff lift and lower legs slowly

(2)

3. Lying stretched out on the floor and keeping the knees stiff and heels touching the floor, lift up the torso, turning to the left with the arms held towards the left. Lie down again slowly. Repeat turning to the right. Relax, and repeat 5 times.

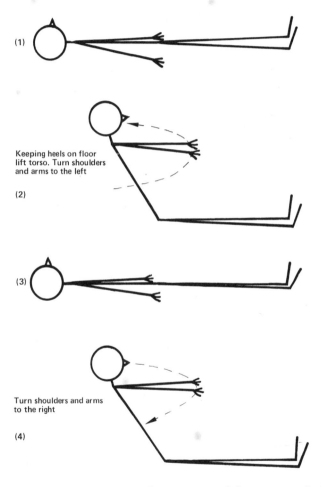

(1)

Keeping heels on floor lift torso. Turn shoulders and arms to the left

(2)

(3)

Turn shoulders and arms to the right

(4)

Some women lose a good contour quickest around the upper thigh and the following exercises (coupled with swimming as often as possible) work wonders in re-shaping them:

1. Lie on the floor chin held up high, hands clasped behind the head, knees bent and feet as close to the body as possible. Keeping the torso flat on the ground, roll from one hip to the other without separating the legs. Start slowly and increase the speed, 10 times in all.

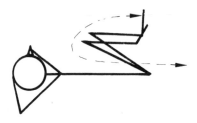

With hands behind head, chin high and knees bent, roll from one hip to the other

2. Lying on the right side with right arm curved under the head, lift both legs in the air as high as possible, then lower them. Repeat 5 times and change to the left side. Repeat 5 times. Start with 5 times each side and increase gradually to 10 times.

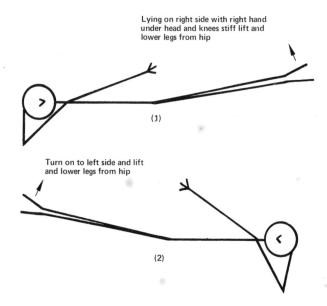

Lying on right side with right hand under head and knees stiff lift and lower legs from hip

(1)

Turn on to left side and lift and lower legs from hip

(2)

3. Sitting up on the floor and leaning back on stiff arms, lift up both legs, knees straight, and execute a scissors movement with the feet and legs quickly 5 times and without bending the knees. Lower the legs and repeat 3 times.

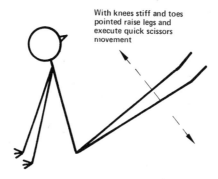

With knees stiff and toes pointed raise legs and execute quick scissors movement

Exercises which tighten up the muscles of the seat are important. So much sitting around in offices and cars can take all the spring out of them. First of all, don't take the lift. Walk upstairs instead whenever possible. Then:

1. Lying on the floor one knee bent, lift up the pelvis and the other leg, straight up in the air keeping the knee stiff at the same time. Hold for 10 seconds. Repeat 5 times and then change to the other leg.

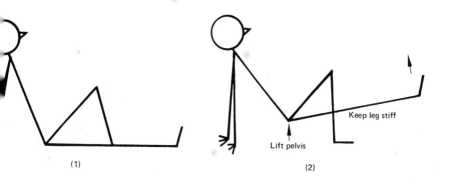

Keep leg stiff

Lift pelvis

(1)   (2)

2. Lying on the floor, face downwards and hand under the chin, lift up both legs, knees stiff, and execute a series of rapid scissors movements with the feet and legs. Repeat 3 times in series of 5 beats. Omit this exercise if you suffer with back trouble.

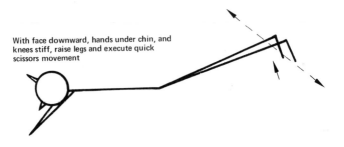

With face downward, hands under chin, and knees stiff, raise legs and execute quick scissors movement

3. Lying on your back lift the legs straight up in the air, supporting the hips on bent arms and make the same scissors movements with the feet, then slowly lower the legs. Repeat 3 times in a series of 10 beats.

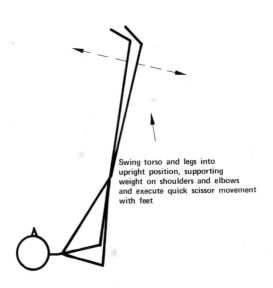

Swing torso and legs into upright position, supporting weight on shoulders and elbows and execute quick scissor movement with feet

When these exercises, after a few weeks, can be performed without effort, pass on to the following which are more advanced.

For the waist, abdomen, thighs and calves:

1. Standing tall, seat tucked in, abdomen held up and in, head up and chin down, walk around the room on the very tip of the toes with the knees stiff. Do this 3 times around the room.

With seat and abdomen tucked in, knees stiff and standing on tip-toe walk around the room

Transfer weight from heels to tip of toes

2. Place an average sized book on the floor, put the toes on the side of it and still in the tall position raise the body until you are standing on the book on tip-toe. Relax, and repeat 5 times.

3. Standing tall, feet apart, lift the right arm high over the head, and slide the left arm down the left thigh bending with it until you can go no further. Repeat 10 times, and then 10 times down the right side.

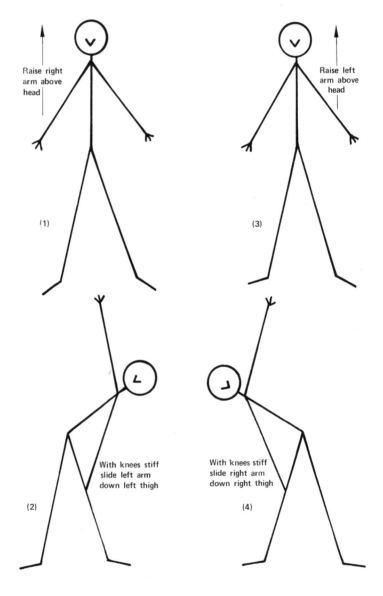

4. Standing tall with feet apart, lift both arms over the head keeping the hands together, and without bending the knees try to touch the left foot. If not at first, then little by little you will achieve it. Return to the original position and repeat to the right side. Repeat 10 times.

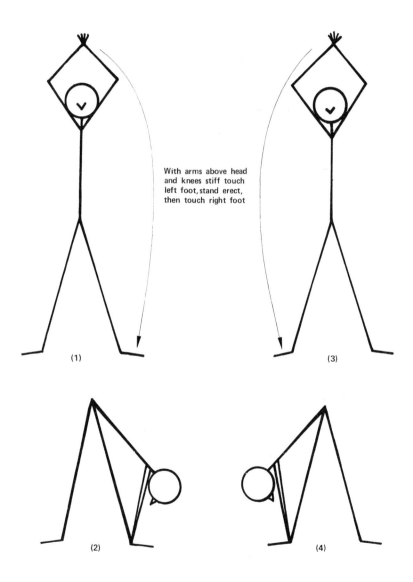

With arms above head and knees stiff touch left foot, stand erect, then touch right foot

(1)

(2)

(3)

(4)

5. Lying on the floor on the left side, with the feet pressed close together and the left arm bent to cushion the head, lift up both legs and the torso pressing down on the ground with the right hand to lift both feet and head as high as possible. Return to original position and repeat 5 times. Turn on the right side and repeat 5 times.

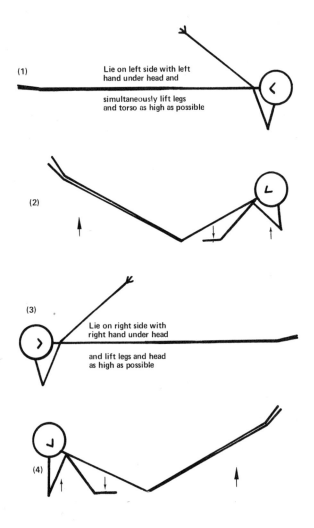

(1) Lie on left side with left hand under head and

simultaneously lift legs and torso as high as possible

(2)

(3) Lie on right side with right hand under head

and lift legs and head as high as possible

(4)

6. Sitting on the floor with the knees bent and feet crossed tailor fashion, turn the torso to the left clasping the left knee with the right hand. Hold this position for 10 seconds pulling the upper body as far round as possible. Relax, and turn to the right. Repeat 10 times.

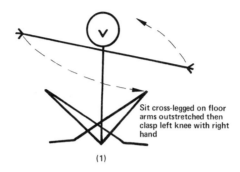

Sit cross-legged on floor arms outstretched then clasp left knee with right hand

(1)

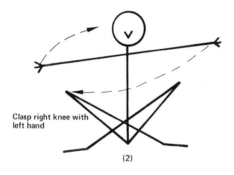

Clasp right knee with left hand

(2)

7. Sitting on the floor lean back on the forearms, bend the knees and draw them up on to the chest. Then knees together, stretch out the legs and lower them to the ground. Repeat 10 times.

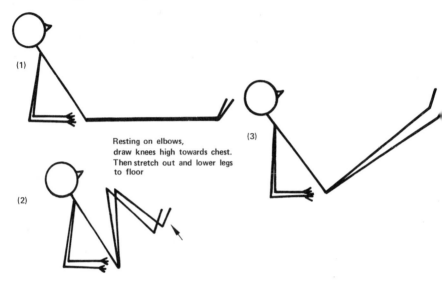

(1)

(2)

(3)

Resting on elbows, draw knees high towards chest. Then stretch out and lower legs to floor

8. Lying flat on the ground lift up both legs to a vertical position and describe large circles with both knees straight and held together. Repeat 10 times.

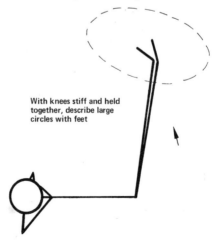

With knees stiff and held together, describe large circles with feet

To regain and retain strength in the muscles which support the breasts there are some invaluable exercises. To carry them out you must provide yourself with a heavy motor car sponge, 3 inches thick and approximately the size of a brick. Fold this in two and hold it between the two palms.

1. Bend the arms at shoulder height with the hands held in front of the chest, and compress the palms smartly together and relax, press and relax, press and relax, 10 times in all.

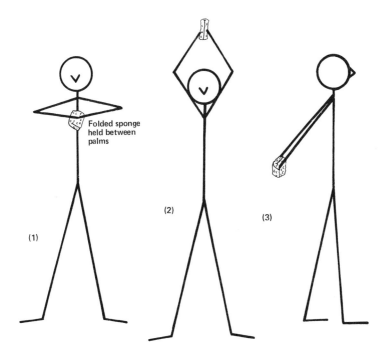

Folded sponge held between palms

(1)

(2)

(3)

2. Hold the arms above the head, palms together holding the sponge, and repeat the exercise 10 times.
3. Holding the hands behind the back repeat the exercise 10 times.

Wearing a good brassière constantly and splashing the breasts with very cold water every morning are two good habits which help, and swimming is the best possible exercise to keep these muscles in trim.

Other exercises can be carried out when the sponge is not available:

1. Standing tall, head up and abdomen held *up* and *in*, hold the arms out in front of the body with the elbows stiff. Describe wide scissors movements with the arms 10 times. Lower the arms and repeat the exercise with the arms held down in front of the body.

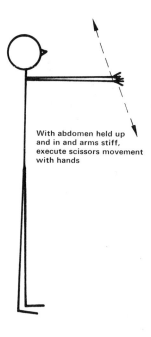

With abdomen held up and in and arms stiff, execute scissors movement with hands

2. Lying down on your back on a narrow table (or 3 lined-up stools) and holding a heavy object in each hand, drop the arms down the sides of the table, then lift them up slowly to full height. Lower them gently, crossing the hands over the chest. Lift the arms up and drop them again down on each side of the body. Repeat 5 times, gradually increasing by one exercise each day until 10 can be repeated.

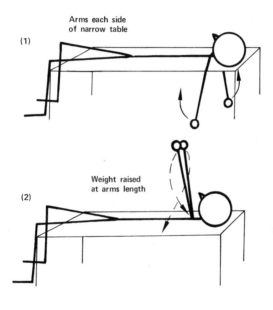

(1) Arms each side of narrow table

(2) Weight raised at arms length

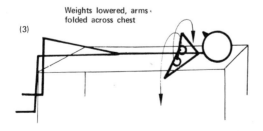

(3) Weights lowered, arms folded across chest

A very good exercise for the neck which helps to retain its suppleness is the following:

1. Drop the chin on the chest relaxing completely as you do so, then roll the head slowly to the right, then back and round to the left before returning to the original position. Repeat starting at the left. Do this exercise 5 times to each side.

Starting with chin on the chest roll head in complete circle, first to the right then to the left

(1)

Standing against a wall lower chin on to chest then raise head to touch the wall

(2)

2. Standing tall against a wall with the back of the neck touching it as near as possible, tuck the chin well in. Relax, lift the chin, and repeat 10 times.

The trim enviable outline of a ballet dancer's waist, hips and thighs are the result of exercises which keep the muscles in perfect condition. Many of these exercises are of great value to the dieter, increasing their muscular control and in consequence their ability when practising any sport.

For the execution of all ballet exercises it is essential to learn the five positions which in themselves repeated five or six times can provide good muscular exercise for the calf, thigh and back muscles. Start by holding on to the back of a chair or the mantelpiece until balance is achieved, and then execute the same exercises standing in the middle of the room. The accompanying arm movements help retain the body's balance.

1st position
Standing tall, hold the back of the chair in the left hand. Place the heels together with the toes pointing outwards in as straight a line as possible. Stretch the right arm down in front of the body and then upwards and outwards in a gentle curve to shoulder height.

2nd position
Lifting the right heel, point the toe and slide the foot outwards about 12 inches away still maintaining a straight line, lower the heel and stand with the weight equally distributed on both feet. At the same time repeat the previous arm movement.

3rd position
Raise the heel of the right foot, point the toe sharply and draw the foot inwards placing the heel under the instep of the left foot. Force both toes outwards to a well turned-out position. Repeat the arm movement at the same time.

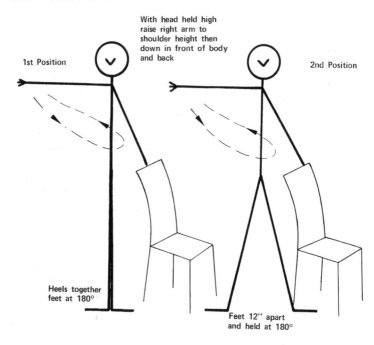

1st Position

With head held high raise right arm to shoulder height then down in front of body and back

2nd Position

Heels together feet at 180°

Feet 12″ apart and held at 180°

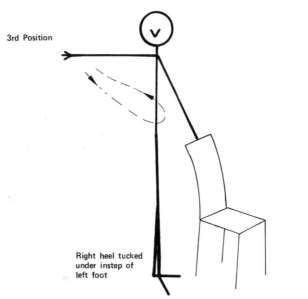

3rd Position

Right heel tucked under instep of left foot

4th position
Raise the heel of the right foot, point the toe and slide the foot forward into a position parallel to the left foot, turning the toes out and thrusting both heels forward while keeping both knees stiff. Repeat the arm movement.

5th position
Raise the heel of the right foot, point the toe and draw the foot back pressing the right heel against the left toe and placing both feet as close together as possible and parallel to each other. Keep the knees stiff and the arm moving as before to end the exercise with it held gracefully above the head, fingers slightly parted, middle finger bent and thumb held closely against the first finger. Hold the head erect at all times and the shoulders down.

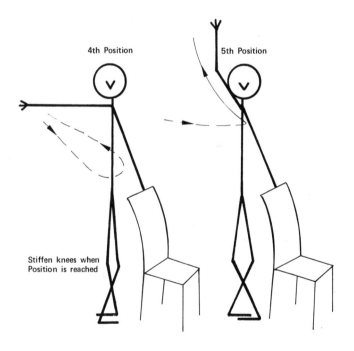

4th Position

5th Position

Stiffen knees when
Position is reached

Turn and repeat the exercises with the left foot.

Now repeat the five positions bending the knees gently and gradually as much as possible in each position. After one week of these exercises it is amazing how much more supple you will be.

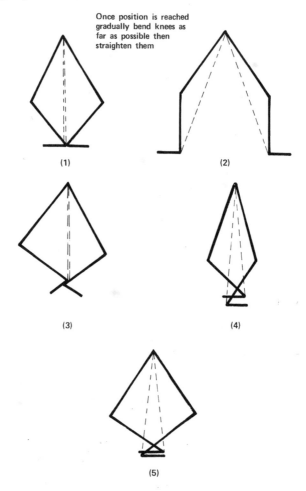

Once position is reached gradually bend knees as far as possible then straighten them

(1)   (2)

(3)   (4)

(5)

When these exercises are executed in the centre of the room use both arms bringing them together, elbows slightly bent, up in front of the body and outwards to be held at shoulder height to maintain the balance. With the last position, the 5th, both arms should be brought upwards and held arched above the head.

Also for fining down the outline of hips and thighs the following movements are excellent:

Grasp the back of a chair rail with the left hand and place the feet in the 1st position, keeping both knees straight.
With toes pointed, sweep the right leg forward up to waist height and back as high as possible keeping the torso upright, and knees straight.
Sweep the right leg forwards and backwards always as high as possible, 10 times in all. As the foot comes down, lift the toes each time so that the foot is at right angles to the leg, brushing one heel against the other and pointing the toe again as the leg is raised. This will work all the muscles of ankle, calf, thigh and hip. Keep the arms outstretched at shoulder height during the exercise.

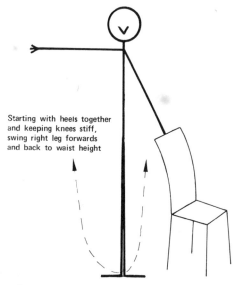

Starting with heels together and keeping knees stiff, swing right leg forwards and back to waist height

Executing these movements to waltz-time music makes them very pleasant to perform.

All the kicking exercises repeated first with the left foot and then with the right while holding on to a chair rail are good for general posture and refining the thighs and hips.

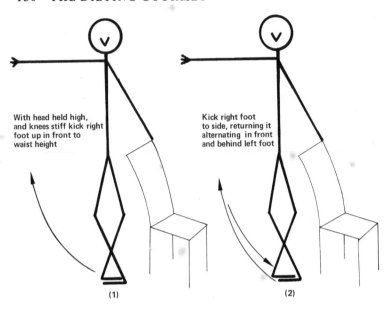

With head held high, and knees stiff kick right foot up in front to waist height

(1)

Kick right foot to side, returning it alternating in front and behind left foot

(2)

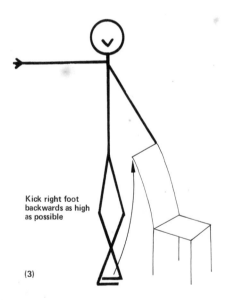

Kick right foot backwards as high as possible

(3)

1. Holding on to the chair rail with the left hand, right arm held outwards at shoulder height, feet in 5th position and knees stiff, kick the right foot up to waist height. Return to 5th position and repeat 5 times.
2. Kick to the side returning the right foot first in front and then behind the left, into the 5th position each time. Repeat 5 times.
3. With the right foot in the 5th position behind the left foot, kick backwards maintaining the torso upright and the head high. Repeat 5 times, then turn and repeat the exercises with the left leg.

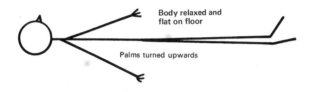

Body relaxed and flat on floor

Palms turned upwards

When resting after executing two or more sets of exercises, lie flat on the floor on your back with the arms lying alongside the body and the palms turned upwards, eyes closed, and all muscles completely relaxed.

Chapter 9

Recipes for Good Looks

If you are put to the 'Desert Island' test insist on being stranded with a good supply of lemons. Apart from their valuable vitamin C content and their use in cooking they are invaluable as a natural beauty aid.

As a most effective pick-me-up for a tired complexion (and the tired liver responsible for it) take the juice of half a lemon in a glass of warm water every morning on an empty stomach for two weeks and notice the difference. The first morning is the hardest. After that the habit grows and the fresh cleansing taste even becomes pleasant.

When the summer holidays are ended and the fading sun-tan makes the skin look neither tanned nor clean but just plain muddy, expedite matters by using a lemon and egg face mask once a week for a month.

LEMON AND EGG FACE MASK
1 large egg
1 large lemon

Separate the egg yolk from the white (this is not used). Squeeze the lemon and beat the juice into the yolk. Spread the mixture on a scrupulously cleaned and dried neck and face avoiding the tender skin under the eyes. Rest for 20 minutes while the mask dries and then wash it off with warm water and splash the face with cold.

The yolks of 2 eggs beaten up with a tablespoon of eau-de-cologne will make an excellent shampoo, and if the hair is given a final rinsing with the juice of a lemon strained into a pint of warm water this will not only make the hair manageable but give it a healthy shimmering gloss as well.

Lemon juice also makes an excellent hand lotion which

keeps the hands soft and white no matter how often the
rubber gloves are forgotten.

LEMON HAND LOTION

3 tablespoons lemon juice   *3 tablespoons lavender water*
3 tablespoons pure glycerine

Put the glycerine in a small bottle and strain the lemon juice on to it. Shake well before adding the lavender water. Shake until the mixture is cloudy each time before use. This quantity can be divided between two small bottles to be kept one in the kitchen and the other in the bathroom. Only a few drops are needed each time after washing the hands.

Another small bottle to be kept in the same two places
should contain this simple but sovereign remedy for the use
of those whose bane is flaking and splitting nails.

NAIL LOTION

8 fluid ounces surgical spirit   *1 teaspoon castor oil*
(22.68 cl)

Shake this mixture very well before use and apply to each nail with a small piece of cotton wool after washing the hands, seven or eight times a day, and give them a thorough treatment last thing at night. It will effect a noticeable change after ten days if applied regularly.

This condition denotes a lack of calcium, and a course of
the Yeast and Yoghurt Diet is the real answer to the
problem. Not only will the figure and nails benefit from it
but the general condition of the skin and hair as well.

There are many fruits and vegetables which can be put
to use as external beauty aids, from the homely potato
to the sophisticated strawberry. Sun-bathing, relaxing and
pleasant as it may be, is not a good thing for the complexion.
It does less harm perhaps to a heavy greasy skin than to a
fine dry skin, but to neither is it beneficial. Dehydration

takes place in every case. Since the sun-tanned face in December has become part of the national one-upmanship these hard facts are overlooked, but the woman who takes time by the forelock and protects her skin while it is still in its prime adjusts the balance in a very simple way.

By rubbing a thick slice of a peeled potato over the face for a few minutes and allowing the juice to dry naturally, both before and after sun-bathing, she gives her skin protection. Using a thick slice of cucumber in the same way will tone and lighten the complexion when the sun-tan starts to fade and a peaches and cream face becomes fashionable.

For those who are seriously concerned by the weather-roughened skin that sailing leaves as a legacy, the following recipe (another legacy) when made up and used regularly will quickly restore softness and clarity to the skin and protect it from further damage.

CUCUMBER SAILING LOTION

3 ripe cucumbers   *¼ drachm powdered borax*
(small size)   *25 drops tincture of benzoin*
¼ Imperial pint rose water
(0.28 litre or 10 fl. oz)

Cut the cucumbers into thick slices but do not peel. Put them into a double boiler or a colander over a saucepan of hot water, cover with a lid and steam until soft. Pass them through an electric liquidiser or a vegetable mill into a large bowl. Measure this pulp and juice and for every 3½ ounces (100 grammes) add the above quantities of rose water, powdered borax and benzoin. Dissolve the borax in the rose water shaking them together in a bottle and adding the benzoin drop by drop, then add this mixture to the pulp, mixing it very thoroughly before bottling.

Apply night and morning and especially before setting sail, rubbing the lotion well into the skin of the face, neck, arms and hands. The results are worth the trouble taken in making the lotion, and though the quantity given may seem large it proves only just enough when a sailing-mad family has to be provided for.

For more delicate use, three or four strawberries crushed to a pulp with a fork and made into a mask with a teaspoon of lemon juice will clear the complexion and leave the skin both looking and feeling fresh. It should be put on to a well-cleaned face and left on while resting for half an hour.

For a greasy skin there is an excellent natural treatment. Put two tablespoons of coarse oatmeal (which can be obtained at any health food store) into a piece of muslin and secure it tightly with a rubber band to make a little pad of the contents. Soak it in a small dish of hot water for an hour and then gently rub it over the face paying particular attention to the sides of the nose, the forehead and crease of the chin. Dip the pad into clean warm water from time to time. When the skin is glowing give it a final rinse with cold water and then, squeezing the pad, pass it again over the face, so that the thin creamy liquid it exudes covers the face entirely. Pat this gently into the skin until it is dry. This oatmeal milk will act as an effective, pleasant astringent and natural powder base. The pad can be used for five or six days before being renewed. In between times keep it with the surface moistened and pressed down in a small dish. Dip the whole pad in warm water and leave it there for a few minutes each time before use.

An effective pick-me-up for dry brittle hair can be made simply by adding 1 tablespoon of eau-de-cologne to 3 tablespoons of good quality olive oil and shaking the two together in a small bottle. When the liquid is cloudy pour no more than three drops into the palm of one hand and rub both palms together before rubbing the ends of the hair between them. Use very little of the lotion at a time and use it every day *on the ends of the hair only*, and an improvement will very soon be noticed.

Reverting to childhood days when each night's bath was a hurried affair not to be dallied over, Saturday bath-night can be recalled with pleasure as a much more leisurely event. Floating toys were allowed and the bath-salts much appreciated. Then with hair freshly washed and with toe and finger nails cleaned and trimmed, one was tucked into bed, shining clean, to settle down for the week's treat of supper in bed and a longer than usual story told while eating it.

A grown-up version of this pleasant ceremony makes one of the best beauty and health treatments on record. An early night, a full eight hours' sleep after a light supper eaten in bed, relaxing with a book after a leisurely bath, all cost nothing and renew the energy so quickly depleted by a week's work in the tension of a crowded dirty city.

Prepare supper beforehand, a large breakfastcup of Beauty Broth made very hot and poured into a vacuum flask, a salad of one variety or another with two slices of crisp bread and a yoghurt with wheatgerm, or if on a more strict diet, an apple, a piece of cheese and a glass of milk.

Run the bath, switch on the electric blanket (warmth is a great relaxing agent), put the prepared tray and that good book on the bedside table and start to get yourself ready.

After cleaning face and neck with scrupulous care wipe them over with a witch hazel-soaked pad of cotton wool. Give the neck only an extra treatment by wiping it over thoroughly with another pad squeezed out in eau-de-cologne. The effect of this (as seen from the pad afterwards) will surprise you, especially in the winter months. Renew the pad and repeat the treatment, reaching as far down the back and between the shoulder blades as possible. This is especially recommended to teenagers who are troubled with spots. For them this should be followed by a face and forehead treatment with an oatmeal pad. For those who have dry or normal skin, this should be replaced by a gentle massage with skinfood.

This is the night for complete relaxation, so before getting into the bath simply fasten the hair into a topknot. Leave the pinning-up torture out of the routine tonight.

Perfumed bath oil is pleasant to use, but a real tonic bath is made by adding a handful of ordinary soda and half a cup of household ammonia to a bathful of hot water and soaking in it for 15 minutes. This was used in the old days as the method of warding off stiffness after a day's hunting, by those who really knew their aches and pains. It will be found invaluable after the daily exercises for the first two or three sessions.

Using a bath-brush shaped to fit the hand or even a soft-bristled laundry brush, and soap, give yourself a good scrub all over until the skin tingles. With a small complexion brush gently stimulate the skin of the face and neck in the same way. This also removes the minute particles of dead skin which accumulate on the surface.

If feeling sufficiently spartan, when you start to let the hot water out, and still lying in it, turn the cold water on until the bath-water is all cold. Then a quick rub with a thick towel, followed by an all-over body massage with a little baby lotion, will leave you glowing.

Enjoy your supper and book and long before your usual bedtime, certainly not later than 9.30 p.m., slowly sip the hot beauty broth, put out the light and settle down for a long night's sleep. You will waken up refreshed and looking forward to the next bath and beauty night.

Beauty nights and a sane diet can do so much towards conserving not only looks and figure but also mental energy and interest in all that life holds.

Which brings to mind the Diet-to-end-All-Diets.

It was practised by one of the most beautiful women I have ever seen, and certainly the most vital, witty and charming. She was a Frenchwoman living in a very prosperous wine-producing area where the town's social life was hectic and international. She never missed a party, a luncheon, a dinner or a ball, but once a year, at the *vendange*, she disappeared to her house in the surrounding countryside. There she closed the doors, gently cultivated the last roses, rested, kept early hours and for three weeks ate nothing but grapes. Starting with a large bunch, she worked up to eating 4 lb of grapes a day, skin, pips and all.

From this retreat she emerged slim, more radiant and more magnetic than ever. Men reeled under the impact of her sexual attraction and with the utmost elegance and discretion she did nothing to prolong the agony of the chosen few. At the time she must have been seventy.

It might be worth a trial.